THE
HOSPITAL ON THE HILL
A CENTURY OF CARE

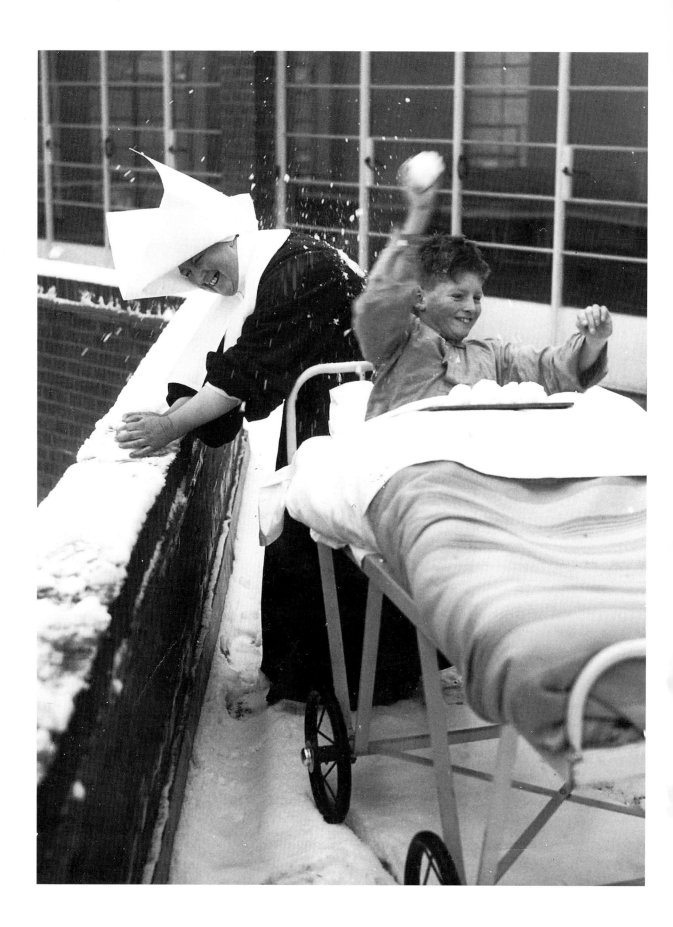

THE HOSPITAL ON THE HILL
A CENTURY OF CARE

ST VINCENT'S ORTHOPAEDIC
HOSPITAL EASTCOTE

To Robby with every best wish

[signature]

JACQUIE SCOTT

Remembering the first 100 years at the hospital placed under
the care of the Daughters of Charity of St Vincent de Paul

Jacquie Scott

Publication in this form © Pitkin Publishing 2014.
No part of this publication may be reproduced, stored in a
retrieval system or transmitted in any form or by any means
without the permission of Pitkin Publishing and the copyright
holders.

ISBN 978-1-84165-569-7

Pitkin Publishing, The History Press, The Mill, Brimscombe Port,
Stroud, Gloucestershire, GL5 2QG.

CONTENTS

ACKNOWLEDGEMENTS

Thanks are due to many people who made this book possible. First and foremost are to Sr Mary Joseph Powell DC, whose energy, enthusiasm, amazing memory and lively interest in all things to do with St Vincent's has kept me going and her never-ending fund of discoveries, mementos, pictures and articles which 'just might be useful for the book' was the result of dedicated and skilled work. Sr Carmel Cussen DC for her energy in searching out the 'modern' past to ensure that dates and names are correct, also to Margaret Bayliss, my aunt, who has patiently heard me talk of 'writing this book' for over a decade!

I am indebted to Irene Heywood Jones who 'did focus on the small stuff with amateur efforts at proofreading'. However, she advises readers 'not to pin their mental well-being on the occasional, yet maddening errors!'

Most of all, of course, I have to thank those people who have been a great part of the rich history of St Vincent's, who have shared memoirs and charming, amusing letters, plus stories of their days involved with St Vincent's. While there will undoubtedly be some omissions I hope to provide a snapshot of this wonderful place: the warmth, love and professionalism that St Vincent's has exuded over the years and that continues under the guidance of the current Matron and Board of Trustees.

St Vincent de Paul and St Louise de Marillac played their part and I hope their spirits continue into the next century.

INTRODUCTION

Between the covers of this book lies a powerful story of growth and achievement – this is not a story without struggles and challenges.

As I reflect on the contribution made by St Vincent's to the lives of so many, I imagine the voices of generations echoing through its corridors and fields. If the walls themselves could speak, they would praise the founding heroes and the thousands who have followed in their footsteps, for their fidelity to the charisma of the founder St Vincent and the Daughters of Charity. They would loudly attest that St Vincent's has served the poor and disadvantaged within London and beyond, and continues to do so with its public benefit charitable contribution as a care home.

Magnificat anima mea Dominum – My soul magnifies the Lord – is our *raison d'être*. Throughout the foundation's 100-year history, the love of Christ has impelled many people at St Vincent's in a mission to offer healing and help to the sick and dying.

Our history is one factor that shapes our identity. In the 21st century St Vincent's is a care home that carries the mission and its values, among which we stress compassion, dignity and excellence. It exists to serve the healthcare of the disadvantaged, in every aspect of their person, providing ministry to body, mind and spirit. Its history of inclusiveness has been complemented by dedication to teaching and learning and the development of orthopaedic surgery worldwide. It has over the years made an enormous contribution to society.

The challenge of this book is to capture each stitch in the magnificent and meaningful tapestry created by those who started the concept in 1906, and I am humbled to be a part of the story.

PRELUDE

The story of St Vincent's Hospital begins before its foundation. In 1623 Vincent de Paul, a 42-year-old French priest, met Louise de Marillac a 32-year-old widow. They co-founded the Company of the Daughters of Charity of St Vincent de Paul on 29 November 1663 to help the sick and the poor, and to organise the ladies within his parish to be effective in their service.

It was so successful that it spread from the rural districts to Paris, and Louise de Marillac began a more systematic training of the women, particularly for the care of the sick. The Sisters, known as the Daughters of Charity, lived in Community in order to better develop the spiritual life and thus more effectively carry out their mission of service in a Christ-like manner. From the beginning, the Community motto was 'The Charity of Christ impels us'.

St Vincent, born April 1581 at Pouy in south-west France, was ordained to the priesthood at the age of 20. His early life was colourful. Shortly after his ordination, he was left a small legacy. Learning that a man in Marseilles planned to swindle him out of it, he set out in pursuit and managed to obtain his money, but, as they were sailing home, he and his companions were captured by Turkish pirates, taken to Tunis and sold as slaves. Merchants examined them like horses, making them walk, trot and run and carry burdens to test their strength.

One of the fellow slaves was a Muslim, an alchemist. The other slave that was captured with St Vincent was a Frenchman who had lost his Christian faith, which St Vincent helped him regain. They both escaped from Tunis, landing in France in June 1607. St Vincent made his way to Avignon, where the powerful archbishop dispatched him to the Papal Court in Rome. Clearly he made a good impression there, for less than two years later the young priest was sent on a mission to the Court of Henri IV in Paris, where he became Chaplain and adviser to the queen and her agent for charitable donations, especially to the hospitals of France.

It was during his time at the Court that St Vincent discovered the two faces of Paris; the wealth and privilege of the nobility contrasted starkly with the wretchedness and distress of the poor. Moving easily through the ranks of the French nobility, St Vincent made it his mission to alleviate the appalling conditions of the needy, both in the towns and in the countryside, where they were suffering from civil war, famine and squalor.

St Vincent's work for the underprivileged earned him the title 'Father of the Poor'. No small part of his life was spent in awakening the social conscience of

the nobility, motivated above all by his faith. In 1625 he founded a community
of priests whom we know today as the Vincentians, and it is said that his secret
to success was 'through the grace of Our Lord Jesus Christ' – that grace which is
given to those who are simple and humble of heart. St Vincent said that simplic-
ity was his Gospel and, in his opinion, humility was the basic requirement for
anyone who wants to love God and the poor.

— PRAYER OF ST VINCENT —

O Lord, You are the eternal law. You rule the entire universe through Your
infinite wisdom. All created forms of government and all laws regulating the
right of way of life come from You. May it please You to bestow Your blessings
on us, to whom You have given the teachings of the Gospel. Amen

THE FIRST GENERATION:
1907 — 1923

The story starts in 1906 with a Norman Franklin Potter, who was running a number of homes and institutions for orphaned Catholic boys around south London. He was asked by the Archbishop of Westminster, Francis Bourne, (later Cardinal Bourne) if he could undertake any work for Catholic crippled boys, as the only such home had recently closed due to lack of funds.

The question had previously been put to other charitable institutions, including the Daughters of Charity of St Vincent de Paul, but all had declined, dreading the financial burden involved. However, Mr Potter obtained the approval of the Archbishop of Southwark, Archbishop Amigo, in whose Diocese he worked. Two ladies from one of his homes – St Hugh's in Thornton Road, Clapham – decided to give the idea a try, and two or three boys were taken into St Hugh's for a time during the winter of 1906.

The arrangements proved inconvenient and a house called Clarence Lodge some distance away was offered rent-free. After the furniture had been delivered, the neighbours protested at the change of use and threatened the owner of Clarence Lodge with an injunction, so the furniture was returned to St Hugh's. At St Hugh's one floor was reserved for the cripples and a temporary kitchen equipped while more suitable accommodation was sought.

In 1909 a subcommittee was formed for the investigation of a number of sites. The subcommittee comprised Miss Margaret Fraser, Major Pereira and Mgr Bidwell, who later became Bishop.

Bishop Bidwell was the Archbishop of Westminster's representative and took a lead part in the commission to ensure land was identified for St Vincent's. He was particularly proud of his association with St Vincent's and often visited. He died in July 1930 and is buried in the small cemetery at St Vincent's.

Major General Sir Cecil Pereira KCB CMG was a member of the Board of Management from the early days, when St Vincent's was a home for crippled boys in Clapham. He joined the Board in 1909 and remained active on it until his death in 1942. He never failed to give St Vincent's and its problems his whole-hearted attention and hard work.

Even while enormous efforts were made to find suitable accommodation the health, well-being and welfare of the boys was still the predominant focus.

Left: Bishop Bourne became
Cardinal Archbishop of
Westminster. He was very much
loved by all associated with
St Vincent's. One of the wings in
St Vincent's Nursing Home is
dedicated to him.

Below: Letter from 1907 written
by Norman Potter to the Sisters
asking them to take on the 'cripples
home'.

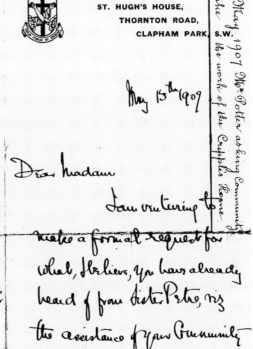

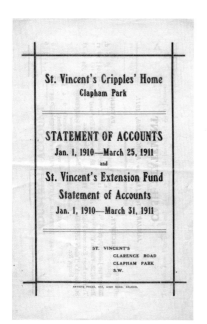

15th Oct. 25th Oct & 8th Nov. 1909.
Mgr. Bidwell re. Cripples' Home

ARCHBISHOP'S HOUSE,
WESTMINSTER,
S.W.

October 15th, 09.

Dear Sister Howard.

The Archbishop desires me to send you the enclosed Memorandum of his views & decision with regard to the Cripples' Home. You will see that the question of the nature of the building has practically settled the matter.

Believe me,

Yours sincerely

1909 correspondence by Bishop Bidwell.

St. Vincent's Cripples' Home
Clapham Park

STATEMENT OF ACCOUNTS
Jan. 1, 1910—March 25, 1911
and

St. Vincent's Extension Fund
Statement of Accounts
Jan. 1, 1910—March 31, 1911

ST. VINCENT'S
CLARENCE ROAD
CLAPHAM PARK
S.W.

CASH STATEMENT

JANUARY 1st, 1910, to MARCH 25th, 1911.

RECEIPTS.	£	s.	d.	PAYMENTS.	£	s.	d.
Balance 1st January, 1910 -	154	12	4	St. Vincent's - - -	2695	16	11
Receipts, St. Vincent's - -	1812	6	4	St. Joseph's Tailors' and Brush			
Transfers from Extension Fund	845	18	1	Shops, &c. - - -	394	14	11
St. Joseph's Tailors' and Brush				Balance in hand (petty cash)			
Shops, &c. - - -	280	3	7	Sister Superior			
				St. Vincent's	2	4	5
				Superintendent			
				St. Joseph's	0	4	1
					2	8	6
	£3093	0	4		£3093	0	4

Above left: Statement of Accounts, 1910–1911.

Above right: Cash statement, 1910/11.

An old coaching house became available at 139 Kings Avenue, Clapham Park, and the lease was purchased. The site is now covered by a block of flats called Prendergast House. Mr Potter again contacted the Sisters of Charity, who now agreed to the proposal and the Home was founded in 1907. St. Vincent's Home for Crippled Boys came into existence, primarily for Catholic boys, although non-Catholics were also admitted. Twenty-five boys were taken from chronic wards and Poor Law institutions and housed in this semi-detached villa in Clapham.

The Board Minutes of 1909 show that Major Pereira had approached Harrods store, regarding the cripples, to enable the boys to earn something through their industry. Harrods felt that toy-making was more of a Christmas industry so not suitable for a permanent trade. With regard to brush-making, Major Pereira said that he was taking samples of brushes with full particulars to the buyer for Harrods. He hoped there might be an opportunity to do trade with Harrods provided the output from the brush shop could be sufficiently large. The Statement of Accounts 1910–1911 indicates the extent of the activity and costs that were already beginning to challenge the Board of Trustees. The general and industrial accounts illustrate a very industrious and proactive home.

During the early 1900s there was considerable uncertainty, needing to maximise resources, the Board decided to create two further subcommittees, the Working Committee and the Industrial Committee. The Working Committee members were the Sister in charge of St Vincent's, Mr Potter, Miss Fraser and Mr Howden; while the Industrial Committee comprised Mr Trapp, Major Pereira and Mr Potter.

In 1910 Rev. R.B. Fellowes was elected to the Board.

In order to ensure boys were given every opportunity to benefit from St Vincent's, the Board agreed in 1910 to the following definition of 'cripples' who were eligible for the Home:

(i)   As to admission. Any child who is handicapped by deformity or loss of limb or who could be benefited by treatment, shall be a suitable subject for the Homes.

(ii) As to retention. That each case be decided on its own merits by the Working subcommittee who should, as far as possible, move out children who have finished with the treatment and who require no special tuition.

Education then became a major concern for all the children. Attaining the Certificate of the Board of Education for the school of St Vincent's was a goal for a further Special subcommittee led by Mr Howden, Rev. Fellowes and Mr Potter. Minutes of the Special subcommittee from May 1910 indicate the thorough approach to ensuring it could be seen as supportive for the children and also sustainable for St Vincent's.

'Physically defective children are considered to be of school age up to 16 and attendance is now compulsory up to that age. The school at St Vincent's must therefore include those boys who are still under 16 years.' The number of children for whom accommodation had to be provided was questioned. It was noted from the Regulations that all children must attend full-time as there was no provision for partial grants. A letter that was signed by Norman Potter shows how the welfare of the boys was the priority.

A grant was 7 shillings per month per child, and this was for 12 months, including holidays. The calculations were: 40 children brought in £168 per year, 30 children £126 and 20 children £84. The headteacher's salary would be at least £100 a year, so there would be little margin if the school had fewer than 40 pupils. The most important immediate step was to get a headteacher appointed.

ST. VINCENT'S GENERAL ACCOUNT

(INCLUDING ST. JOSEPH'S)

JANUARY 1st 1910, to MARCH 25th, 1911.

RECEIPTS.	£	s.	d.	PAYMENTS.	£	s.	d.
To Balance brought forward	154	12	4	By Housekeeping	1124	5	5
Subscriptions	91	0	0	„ Rates, Taxes, Insurance and Ground Rent	196	2	0
Donations	399	1	5	„ Wages, &c.	354	12	6
Collections in Churches	64	10	5	„ Furniture and Repairs	138	2	10
Payments for Boys	1240	15	6	„ Fuel and Light	192	1	10
Amt. transferred from Extension Fund	845	18	1	„ Laundry	98	16	2
Interest from Japanese Bonds set apart for Endowment of Bed	16	19	0	„ Clothing	152	13	7
				„ Medical Expenses	168	11	2
				„ Chaplain's Stipend	53	19	4
				„ Printing, Postage, Stationery, Telephone, and other Office expenses	97	12	8
				„ Travelling & Parcels, Holidays & Entertainments	39	5	2
				„ Pocket Money	12	14	9
				„ Chapel Expenses (including Furniture)	25	8	7
				„ Education	16	13	11
				„ Sundries, Bank Charges, &c.	24	17	0
					2695	16	11
				Industrial a/c Deficit	114	11	4
				Balance in hand	2	8	6
	£2812	16	9		£2812	16	9

Above and below: The school room at Clapham Park.

The Board was required to keep full details of each child's progress and his family history. It was also noted that a different kind of education apart from classes was needed for children on frames. The Board was very reasonable about modifications to the curriculum as long as the schooling met the minimum requirement that each child receive full-time education.

In the 19th century orphans were not only defined as children without parents. Very often orphans were the neglected children of single parents, families in financial arrears or homeless children found living on the streets. Sometimes children sought out orphanages – some being called asylums back then – because the living conditions were better than in their own families. Unfortunately, orphanages were scarce and many children were left to fend for themselves. The orphanage system changed dramatically in the 1900s, making way for revised child labour laws, adoption services, the development of foster care and vocational training.

There was no shortage of very poor families in the early 1900s, but they were not skivers. Some families lived in perpetual poverty, even when the wage earner was in full-time work. Work typically brought in about £1 a week in the poorer parts of London, although it was not reliable. If there was no work, men would be laid off without notice.

The rent for accommodation was around 6–8 shillings a week for one or two rooms in fairly large tenement blocks. As a proportion of family income, such rents were significantly higher than for better-off families. What remained for food and funerals left very little for the other necessities of life, with absolutely nothing for bettering themselves.

The cheapest rooms were in basements, which were always damp and never saw daylight, and tended to be bug infested, so disease and early death was rampant. Most families were large, which meant being creative with the space available. Babies tended to sleep with their parents and children slept two, three or more to a bed, often top to toe.

The women worked hard and the rooms were described as surprisingly clean in the circumstances. Clothing was second-hand and repeatedly mended, and it was normal to see children and even women without shoes.

People were in a community of family, friends and neighbours whom they knew and who knew each other and could be relied upon to help in times of need. To move elsewhere would be to move among strangers.

The Home for Crippled Boys in Clapham was created at the right time, as there came a clear change in emphasis in parts of the medical world from 'minding' to 'curing'. The work done by Sir Robert Jones and Dame Agnes Hunt came to the notice of the Committee. Sir Robert, nephew of Sir Hugh Owen Thomas, the father of orthopaedics, was invited to see the boys.

Applications for admission were obtained from the Hon. Secretary, Rev. R. Fellowes. Applicants were considered by the Committee, and children were accepted with all types of deformity and with diseases giving rise to deformity where treatment could improve the condition and make the patient fit to earn his living. These included all forms of surgical tuberculosis, chronic infective diseases of bones and joints, poliomyelitis, cerebral palsy (except where the child was mentally deficient), congenital and acquired deformities such as club feet and spinal curvature, and deformities due to rickets or resulting from accidents.

St. Vincent's Cripples' Home claims support <u>from all</u> because crippled boys <u>from all parts</u> are benefited by it.

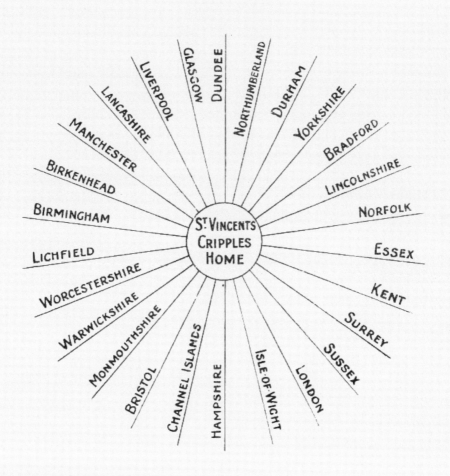

Cripples from the above localities are being maintained at St. Vincent's Home in the present year.

Above: St Vincent's Cripples' Home – diverse catchment.

Left: St Vincent's Open-Air Surgical & Industrial Home, 1909.

The severity of the case was never a bar to admission, for practically no deformity was incapable of being improved by specialist treatment. Bony deformities, whether resulting from old tuberculosis, rickets or septic osteo-arthritis, could usually be corrected so that little or no deformity was apparent after treatment. In the case of tubercular disease it was noted that (1) under proper treatment, especially in the open air, deformity could nearly always be prevented and (2) the earlier the case came under treatment the better the result. For example, in 16 cases of tubercular hip disease only two cases had more than one inch of apparent shortening.

A typical case, who had had no treatment previously, was treated successfully, despite a 3½-inch shortening, flexion deformity of 90%, marked adduction, complete ankylosis of hip and flexion of knee. Although children were admitted suffering from abscesses and wounds of all kinds, there were few dressings and the general health and well-being of all in the Home were excellent.

The Home, which was rented, consisted of two houses in Clapham Park, with adjoining grounds. The surgical home where the open-air treatment was carried out comprised a house with 7 acres of land. The industrial home was situated in much smaller grounds. The combined area covered 10 acres and in the garden a hut/shed and tents were erected pending the removal of the entire establishment from Clapham to a more suitable site in the country.

The Cripples' Industries described itself in 1912:

> A bootmakers' and tailors' shop with competent instructors form part of the Industrial Home in which the cripples are trained to earn their own living. Wood-carving, basket-making, knitting are also taught, with most satisfactory results. Though a Catholic Home and primarily for Catholic children, non-Catholic children are admitted for treatment at St Vincent's. No suitable case is refused admission as long as accommodation can be found in the Home and funds permit.

There were very few institutions of the kind in this country, and St Vincent's Home was the only one under Catholic management entirely devoted to the treatment of crippled boys. The establishment became known as St Vincent's Hospital and Home for Crippled Boys. In 1910 the first advertisements offering the facilities of the Home were published.

The cost of treatment was by its very nature expensive, and the Local Government Board fixed £30 as a reasonable annual charge in respect of the maintenance, clothing and education of crippled boys sent to the Home and for others the medical charge of £20 16s.

Though high when compared to the amount allowed for maintenance in ordinary certified schools, the sum compared favourably with the cost for crippled children in other Surgical Homes. Subscriptions and donations were desperately needed, however, as in many cases it was impossible to obtain the full cost for the child's maintenance and treatment, while in some instances no payment of any kind was received. Despite the fact that the new charges could not be met by some patients there was no bar to the treatment and services offered.

The St Vincent's Cripples' Home Association was formed in 1912 to raise money from voluntary sources to pay for the keep of those boys for whom no other funds were available.

Sir Robert Jones (1857–1933) was not only a great and kind man but quite possibly the greatest orthopaedic surgeon the world has ever seen. Family poverty sent him as an apprentice to Sir Hugh Owen Thomas and he confined himself to orthopaedic surgery from 1905.

Initially his surgical technique was to rely on reduction under general anaesthetic then traction, alignment and immobilisation, using splints rather than plaster. However, the discovery of X-rays by Roentgen in December 1895 made him view the management from a different perspective. He bought a machine in May 1896 and was probably the first man to take an X-ray in Britain.

In the early 20th century, Jones introduced the immediate reduction of fractures, a major shift in treatment which improved healing and recovery. He emerges as a man of immense stature, energy, tact and vision. Jones instigated the foundation of the British Orthopaedic Association in 1926 with which the future St Vincent's Hospital continued to be closely linked.

Orthopaedic surgeons. Seated left to right: Harry Platt, Muirhead Little, Robert Jones, David McCrae Aitken, W. Bennett; standing: Rowley Bristow, Mr Girdlestone, Mr Emslie.

Robert Jones believed that few children were so incurable that they could not become well if placed in proper circumstances for treatment. By this he meant dedicated hospitals providing specialist care, and this is what he set out to create. Robert Jones was invited to meet Sr Teresa Fraser DC and visit the crippled boys, and so the challenge began.

As a result of philanthropic efforts, Robert Jones started his work in Liverpool in 1900 and subsequently supported other institutions: Baschurch in Oswestry, later to become the Robert Jones and Agnes Hunt Hospital (1933), Chailey (1903), Lord Mayor Treloar, Alton (1908) and, of course, St Vincent's Surgical Home in Clapham (1906).

The First World War interrupted schemes for the welfare of 'cripples' but the development of orthopaedics improved the advancement of surgical invention, particularly during the period 1914–1918. Robert Jones became a Captain in the reserve and was soon promoted to Major and toured hospitals in the Western Command. He was horrified by the number of soldiers wounded and requiring orthopaedic surgery.

He went on to influence and train the next generation of orthopaedic surgeons in the post-war years. Robert Jones took up honorary appointments with the Royal National Orthopaedic Hospital in 1918 and St Thomas' Hospital in 1919 and continued a private practice in London whilst still maintaining his visits to other hospitals to provide clinical advice. Sir Robert Jones died in 1933.

An orthopaedic surgeon who worked alongside Robert Jones in Liverpool was Mr D. McCrae Aitken. He visited St Vincent's Home in 1910 and saw a number of sickly and totally dejected boys making brushes in the old coach house. Of those 25 he selected 19 for immediate treatment, and within three years 12 of them were earning their own living. A few years earlier this would have been unthinkable! Mr McCrae Aitken subsequently became the principal surgeon at Eastcote and served there for 36 years.

Sister Teresa Fraser DC, who became the first Matron and lived to the age of 103 (1897–1990), trained as an orthopaedic nurse. Her skills and knowledge were invaluable at that time, working tirelessly alongside the surgeons to achieve independence for the boys. Sir Robert Jones was the first Honorary Surgeon at St Vincent's until his death in 1933.

All boys in the Home had been accepted because they were regarded as incurable, so the most that could be done was try to give them a basic education and occupy their minds. The boys came to the Home from the slums and workhouses in London's poorest areas where cripples were regarded as social outcasts and their chance of survival was very slim. The Homes were kept going by charitable donations and church collections. There were also two clinics in London, one in Victoria and another in Bow.

Sister Teresa Fraser, first Matron at
St Vincent's, Pinner, *c.*1911.

The object of bringing children together under one roof was to care for them
with Christian love and give them some education and interest in a vocational
activity. The Daughters of Charity were eminently suited to this work. It was
clearly a forward-thinking approach to the holistic theory of caring for mind,
body and soul in terms of supporting and healing – a principle that is still mod-
elled in current healthcare.

— SISTERS OF CHARITY OF ST VINCENT DE PAUL —

The Community of the Daughters of Charity of St Vincent de Paul was founded
in 1633 in France by St Vincent and Louise de Marillac. Their official title is
'Daughters of Charity', and they are known as such in the USA and Australia, but
in Great Britain and Ireland they are the Sisters of Charity.

On 29 September 1633, Madame le Gras, whose maiden name was Louise de
Marillac, and four young women moved into a house in Paris, so founding the
first House of the Community. Louise de Marillac was born in 1591 and died on
15 March 1660, six months before St Vincent. She was canonised in 1934.

In St Vincent's day the word 'religious' or 'nun' signified 'enclosure'. But his
'Daughters' were allowed to go everywhere to work with people in any kind of
need, especially the poor and sick. The novitiate of the Daughters of Charity is
known as the 'Seminary', their dwellings are called 'Houses' not 'Convents', and
the duty assigned them is called their 'Office'. To the vows of poverty, chastity and
obedience they add a fourth: 'service to the poor'.

St Vincent told his first Daughters that the chief purpose for which God had called them was to honour Our Lord Jesus Christ as the source and model of all charity, serving Him corporally and spiritually in the person of the poor. He wished the spirit of prayer to be strong among them, that even amidst the most distracting occupations they would be united to Him.

THE MIRACULOUS MEDAL

On 27 November 1830 Our Lady appeared in an apparition to Catherine Laboure and said, 'Have a medal struck on this model. All who wear it will receive great graces' and so a special medal was struck. It was first distributed in May 1832.

HISTORICAL ELEMENT

Apparitions are unusual, and yet they are dramatic reminders of what was going on at the time. About midnight on 18 July 1830, Catherine Laboure (novice Daughter of Charity) was led to the chapel of Rue du Bac in Paris and there spoke with the Mother of God. In a dramatic way she experienced the care and affection which Our Lady has for everyone but especially for those who bear the name of her Son and call themselves Christians.

Catherine was given a task. Four months later, on 27 November, she was shown the design of a medal which would remind people of the love and protection which Our Lady offers us. Wearing the medal would be our gesture of acceptance.

A picture on page 24 shows the medal. On the front is a woman, the Mother of God, encircled by a short and famous prayer. 'O Mary conceived without sin, pray for us who have recourse to thee'. Being 'conceived without sin', often referred to as her Immaculate Conception, means that from the first moment of her exist-ence, Mary was preserved from sin in all its forms. Filled with God's grace, the saving work of her Son was fully active in her, even before it took place. Now, with a mother's attention, she continually brings us the fruits of that work. On the back of the medal we see a large letter M with a cross above it. M is for Mary and Mother. The two hearts are those of Jesus and Mary. This is to remind us of God's love for us; Mother and Son united in the work of redemption as Christ offers himself on the Cross and Mary stands by that Cross, assenting in faith so that the world might be saved.

The medal is no 'good-luck charm'. It is a reminder that Our Lady is, as Pope Paul VI said:

> a sure hope for those troubled in mind as they often are; divided in heart; uncertain before the riddle of death; oppressed by loneliness; a prey to boredom.

(Courtesy of the Daughters of Charity of St Vincent de Paul)

THE MANY SIDES OF THE MIRACULOUS MEDAL

Catherine Laboure lived an ordinary, obscure, laborious life as a Daughter of Charity in the 19th century, and no one, except her confessor, knew that it was she who had received from Our Lady the request to have the Miraculous Medal made and distributed. The Daughters of Charity and the Vincentian Fathers have since publicised and promoted the medal and its message to the world, and an enlarged model of the medal welcomes visitors at the doors to the Chapel in St Vincent's Nursing Home.

The Daughters of Charity first entered England in 1847. However, despite Catholic emancipation in 1829, England was still not ready to embrace them, so they returned to France. It was far from an easy task. The Daughters of Charity suffered extreme poverty and were often surrounded by hostility. In London, their first house was rat infested and they had to move. They were in constant financial problems, but – undeterred – they cared for those who needed help.

They returned to England in 1857, arriving in York Street, Marylebone, London in 1859, settling in Park Street in 1860 and moving to Carlisle Place, London in May 1863, where, through the generosity of the Dowager Duchess of Norfolk, the Sisters started a soup kitchen providing hundreds of sick and destitute with a bowl of hot soup and piece of bread per day throughout the cold winter months.

The first of the many charity fundraising events began in 1862 in Farm Street Church off Berkeley Square.

When they became involved with these crippled boys, the Sisters already had a number of homes and centres in England looking after some boys, but mainly girls who, for one reason or another, were homeless. So the Sisters were experienced in dealing with children and were used to keeping their homes going by charitable donations and church collections.

With the discovery of open-air treatment it appeared that the hopelessness normally attributed to the lot of the cripple could be overcome and, as a first move, much to the discomfort of the boys in the house, all the window frames were removed. The necessity of open-air treatment was now fully realised, especially in cases of tuberculosis.

Knowing that a future of sorts could be possible for the boys, a site in the country was being sought away from the dampness and smog of London. While the search was being made, another house nearby was purchased and large wooden sheds were erected in the garden. These were the first open-air wards, built entirely of wood and with only three sides – the south-facing side was completely open to the elements.

The boys of school age were transferred to the new sheds, or wards, while the original Home was renamed St Joseph's and retained the older boys. These older boys still received treatment, but were also taught trades, such as tailoring and brush-making.

Above left: Miraculous Medal.

Above right: The homes were 'homes' in the fullest sense of the word. A modern kitchen, 1910-style, from the Clapham Home.

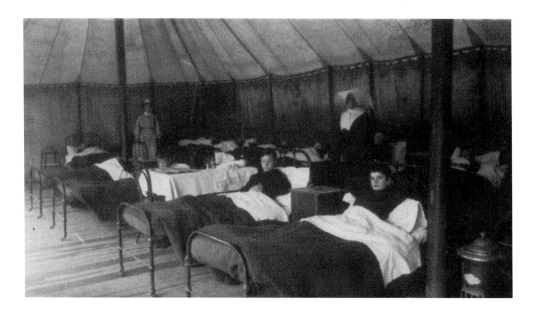

St Vincent's Cripples' Home, Clapham.

Mr Peter Joyce, having been associated with St Vincent's for over 26 years, gives us an insight into those early days, showing that the love and warmth that St Vincent's is so well known for was very much in evidence:

I can still remember arriving at a house in King's Avenue, Clapham Park, on a very wet day in May, and being warmly welcomed by the Sister in charge. She took me into a large room which turned out to be the school and playroom and introduced me to the boys, numbering about a dozen. In the evening I was taken into the garden where I noticed two tents, one containing six beds and the other about thirty.

At the time of my arrival, there were 44 patients and staff consisted of four Sisters and only one nurse.

In the following August the whole of the Home went to Whitstable for a month's holiday. I was terribly excited and greatly enjoyed the novelty of travelling in a special train.

Another event in the October particularly stands out in my memory. A friend who stayed with us for over 20 years came to us from Ireland. I am referring to Paddy the donkey.

How we used to wrangle and nearly fight to be the lucky one to ride him and be able to go on a Saturday to Spiers & Ponds for the vegetables.

He had his own wicked sense of humour – not only did he know every trick there was to know about un-seating his rider, he also knew the precise whereabouts of every holly bush in the grounds, but despite his upsetting habits, we all loved to ride him.

Above: Dining room, Clapham.

Left: Mr Bagnell in front of St Vincent's main reception; note that the Chapel is not built yet.

Above left: Clapham Park – the children and pony play in the fresh air.

Above right: St Vincent's, Pinner, in the early days, *c.*1911.

Above left: Front steps of Clapham Park in the 1900s.

Above right: St Vincent's Cripples' Home – a group photograph before the trip to Pinner.

The next year brought the excitement of moving into a larger house in the next road, with a garden, a big field and a pond. It also boasted electric light and a gas geyser which was apt to go wrong. I can remember it blowing up while a nurse was taking a bath; fortunately no one was hurt.

The older boys were given a younger one to take charge of to ensure that he kept himself tidy and such like, and my particular charge was Jack Bufton. As a St Joseph's boy I was also allowed pocket money.

St Hugh's used to play football matches on our field, and we all used to watch and enjoy them, but we had to keep very quiet as the neighbours objected to having their Sabbath disturbed.

Talk of Pinner and all its wonders kept us anxious for the day we were to go there. This, as days do, eventually came and the ride was unforgettable. It took eight hours and we filled six horse brakes. Being used to London with all its houses, the country seemed like a fairyland.

— TRANSITION TO PINNER —

In 1910 two possible sites in the country came on the market and, after much thought, the site at Eastcote, near Pinner, was chosen. By December 1910, 25 acres were purchased with a 10% deposit of the asking price of £6,000. The site contained a large country house and a brick-and-tiled lodge at the entrance with a quarter-mile carriage drive joining both houses. The Home's name was changed to Ruislip Cripples' Home.

The Minutes of the Statutory Committee of 21 March 1911 held at Archbishop's House, Westminster, reported:

RUISLIP CRIPPLES' HOME

Report of the purchase Subcommittee	
Cost of site	6000
Estimated cost of move and installing	2500
	———
Total	8500
Extension fund	2000
Donation	1000
Balance required	5500

The extension fund was used to part purchase the site. The balance of £5500, and it is hoped to be materially reduced by appeal, would be raised on the value of the site from a banker. The property was put into the name of the first two Trustees, Captain Stirling and Mr Coppinge, followed by Mr Cave and the Archbishop of Westminster. The name of the new Home was reviewed and it was agreed to name it 'The Eastcote Cripples' Home' instead of Ruislip as that was the postal district, and that the name 'St Vincent' sought to be maintained.

With the purchase of the house confirmed and contracts signed on 25 March 1911, Mr Potter relinquished his interest in the Home, and Mr Fellows became Secretary.

Ruislip Holt estate agent's particulars.

Much building had to be done pending the move; wooden wards, the boys' refectory, the operating theatre and X-ray equipment and other necessary buildings and equipment costing a further £2,550. The Home would house 40 boys.

The main reason for choosing the Eastcote site was its advantageous position. With the exception of some red roofs, the views are much the same today. On a clear day the transmitting pylon at Crystal Palace can be easily seen, as can the Hog's Back beyond Guildford. The air is still clear, with very little passing traffic.

With the move to Eastcote, the annual charge per patient rose to 30 guineas (£31.50).

The house and grounds known as Ruislip Holt was formerly part of the Glebelands of the pre-Reformation vicarage of St Martin's at Ruislip. The large country house was owned by Mr Benjamin Davies and situated on Hask Hill (now Haste Hill). Together with the house the Board purchased 25 acres of land on the west side of Wiltshire Lane (then known as Wood Lane). It stood 300 feet above sea level with uninterrupted views to the south. The great landmark of Harrow Hill was 7 miles away and could be seen and the Hog's Back – although some 30 miles away in Surrey – was also clearly visible. The other parcel of land opening on to Fore Street (then called Frog Lane) is now occupied by a garden centre and riding stables.

In about 1806, when the Ruislip Commons were being enclosed, the Vicar of Ruislip had received another 25 acres of Park Wood in lieu of tithes. The trees were cut down and never replanted. In 1893 the Rev. T.M. Everett, then Vicar of Ruislip, redeemed the land tax on this parcel and, with the sanction of the Ecclesiastical Commissioners, granted a 99-year lease to Mr C.W. Millar, who was then residing at Sunnyside, opposite Haydon Hall, Eastcote.

Pinner view, looking towards Harrow.

Presumably Mr Millar built the house known as Ruislip Holt which became the nucleus of the hospital buildings. It is known that both the Welsh tenor Mr Ben Davies and Mr J.R. Cooper, a London magistrate, had lived there during its history. This is the site that St Vincent's came to purchase in 1910.

Meanwhile, back in Clapham in 1911, 90 boys were occupying two houses and had overflowed into a marquee on the lawn in the garden, demonstrating the demand for this new service.

However, during the following winter it was noticed that the general health of the boys in the marquee had greatly improved, despite being situated in a low-lying and particularly foggy district of London. The boys in the house showed no such improvement.

One night, that benefit to the health of the boys in the marquee was dramatically reversed when a strong wind blew down the marquee, burying its hapless occupants in canvas, many of whom were strapped to orthopaedic frames. Needless to say the boys loved every minute of it! The work at that time was mainly the care of crippled children, most of whom were victims of tuberculosis and polio. Those boys of school age who could leave the wards received full-time education in the new home, while the others were taught on the wards.

One boy funded by the Association was Frank Shelley, who very clearly and fondly reflects on his life at St Vincent's spent in both Clapham and in Eastcote. He is proud of starting out with the Clapham boys and in fact indicates that the younger 'Vincentorians' were somewhat jealous or envious of the Clapham boys initially:

> I arrived at St Vincent's (Clapham) on a summer day in 1912, straight from a hospital in Sevenoaks where I had already spent three years. Needless to say the Sisters at once filled me with awe on account of their cornettes headdress, never having seen their like before.
>
> My first pal was Peter Sabatini who was confined to bed. Sab, as he was known, told me that because I had half an inch shorter on one leg I would be going on a frame! For at least three days I was in no small state of bewilderment and terror at this prospect and spent hours looking at the picture frame above my bed, wondering how I was going to be fixed to a similar but larger thing, which goes to show how simple I was! An easy mistake for a child.
>
> George Bearcroft and I between us had a great collection of 5,000 'fag-cards' including some fine sets, and our hearts bled when, on account of measles, they all had to be burned with the rest, amounting to about 50,000.

Mr Shelley continues:

> There were about 14 of us living in a marquee for some months prior to leaving Clapham. It had a wooden floor and underneath which were swarms of rats,

which we used to entice out with bits of food tied on cotton strings and we even named some of them.

I was walking about in a plaster for a couple of months before we came to Eastcote and when we did arrive, at what for us was a kind of Mecca, some losing ourselves in the woods (known to us for many years as 'the forest') and others getting lost in the fruit trees in the orchard.

We had a lot of really enjoyable unpleasantness for the first few days; porridge in cups, ants running over the bread and dripping, mattresses on the floor, school in the refectory.

There were no paths, only clay, and there were hurdles to keep us to tracks that eventually became paths.

I used to like to sit in the branches of the tree at the entrance to the bottom field and read, especially on a Sunday morning, when the sound of the bells from the old church in Ruislip floated across the tree tops and somehow seemed to fit in with the tale I was reading.

There are hundreds of things to write about; the zoo visits, the nature walks, outings with Chaplain, Fr Hurley, the wreck of the aeroplane on Thirty Acres, Mr Glynn, our school plays such as 'Caractacus', Nurse McNicholl, 'Tim of Eastcote', 'Billy Buttons', Miss Twoomey, Miss Killen, Sr Gertrude, Sr Clare, Sr Benedict – all these names call up memories of a happy boyhood and a home of friendly ghosts.

The Eastcote Cripples' Home, 1912

On 1 May 1912 a Deed was enrolled in the Central Office of the Supreme Court of Judicature. The Deed named three Trustees as the new legal owners of the house and grounds and set out the regulations by which the charity known as the Eastcote Cripples' Home was to be governed.

The Trustees, always to be three in number, had to include the Archbishop of Westminster and did so until the 1990s, when this was altered. The Trustees and a majority of the Board of Management had to be Roman Catholics. The Board had to consist of six members nominated by the Trustees and up to six co-opted members: 'The Object of the Charity is to provide medical and surgical treatment for crippled children whether invalid or healthy and to provide for their maintenance, education and industrial training in such a manner and subject to such regulations as from time to time be approved by the Board of Management'. The words 'and adults' were inserted some 30 years later and the Deed still governs the administration of St Vincent's today.

In May 1912 all was ready and the move was made. The journey from Clapham took eight hours, and the boys and staff rode in six horse brakes.

St Vincent's before the First World War.

An aerial perspective of St Vincent's. This is the house, Ruislip Holt, with the addition of the Chapel.

Sr Teresa Fraser DC (Matron) and her sister, Lady Encombe, and Chaplain, *c.*1920s.

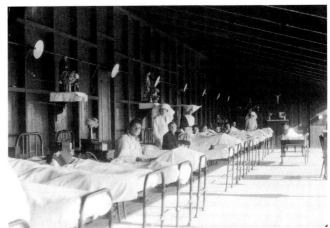

Above: Sr Teresa Fraser DC and her sister Lady Encombe.

Top right: St Vincent's, Pinner — wooden ward (hut).

Centre right: Wooden hut-ward, south-facing, 1912.

Bottom right: Children on the ward; note the blind on the post to protect them from the weather.

Laundry in the early days.

View of the laundry and one of the staff.

Mr Charlie Carey, head gardener, proudly holding his long service medal.

Frank Shelley recalled how several of the vehicles were stuck in the mud, and young patients like himself had to be carried up the hill.

New arrivals were collected from the local station and taken to the Home by pony and trap. The station is on the Metropolitan Line, which was extended from Harrow to Uxbridge in 1906. When it was opened it was called Eastcote Halt.

One particularly sickly boy, who was five when he moved as a patient to St Vincent's, was Jack Sayer. He was desperately ill and, having been given up for dead on many occasions, travelled the whole journey on the lap of the Matron, Sr Teresa. The boy survived, to everyone's amazement, and after years of treatment he chose to stay on at the hospital and eventually joined the staff as a chauffeur for 35 years. He lived until 1977. Charlie Carey was another patient. He took charge of the extensive gardens and grounds, progressing to head gardener. He worked for St Vincent's for 40 years.

In 1892 a Select Committee of the House of Lords recommended that almoners – the first hospital social workers – should be appointed to control overcrowding in hospital outpatient departments. Sr Teresa Fraser of the Daughters of Charity was the first almoner and her duty was to ensure that the boys who were in poor circumstances were helped to benefit from treatments recommended by the medical staff.

Her remarkable reports show that it was the aftercare and assistance of every kind that was given to boys in need that made the difference between survival or not. These were groundbreaking times and the staff were pure pioneers of the support we take for granted in our 'modern' society.

From the very beginning the Home was almost entirely self-sufficient in its food requirements, and this situation lasted for many years.

Older boys were trained on the hospital farm as well as in the workshops, whilst others trained in office work.

In 1914 prices in general were rising rapidly due to the war, and the hospital's survival increasingly depended on voluntary contributions and fundraising events from funfairs, bazaars, jumble sales and charity balls.

The 1916 directions to the Home make interesting reading. They say that the Home is 1 mile distant from Northwood Station by footpath, a route only recommended in dry weather. An alternative route was to Eastcote Halt, where cabs could be specially ordered from the local livery stables. Once the boys arrived at the Home, they were met in the glasshouse by Mother Superior, who would take them to the kitchen for a good meal and then take them to their ward.

On admission to St Vincent's the boys were required to bring the following outfit (this was only for boys at this time): two suits of clothes, three pairs of stockings, three shirts, three night shirts, three vests, two pairs of boots, six handkerchiefs, one pair of slippers, braces and cap, or £2 in money in lieu of the outfit.

The very young went to Holy Child Ward. The boys had a great pastime of mud-slinging contests. A piece of mud was attached to a very pliable cane and the idea was to see whose lump of mud was propelled the furthest. One day in 1916 one of these missiles went somewhat astray, landing on the roof of the glasshouse with a loud bang and that game came to a very abrupt end with the rapid appearance of Mother Superior.

Boys were treated to outings, many of which were arranged by the Northwood Special Constables and opposite you see a charabanc well loaded for such an event. The Royal Tournament was a favourite excursion.

The School Register, which was formally opened on 26 August 1912, indicated that over the years many boys were treated to great outings.

Opposite you see a wooden ward at Eastcote, its style a copy of those built at Clapham. A door at the end led to a small room which was the home of the Sister in charge of the ward. She was, like any mother, on call 24 hours a day; feeding, treating and teaching them by day and comforting them if they were restless at night. A door in the rear wall led to the kitchen, where Sister prepared the meals, and where the only source of heating lay. In later years, heavy half-length canvas curtains were added as a form of luxury but these remained open day and night, unless there happened to be a blizzard aiming into the ward. All wards had uninterrupted views to the south, towards Crystal Palace, of up to 20 miles on a clear day.

The extract from the School Register for 1912, seen on p.38, indicates the conditions that the staff and boys faced – in particular on 10 February 1912.

There can be few 'Old Boys' of St Vincent's who would not know Michael Quinn. The 11-year-old boy arrived at Clapham on 9 February 1912 with both legs paralysed, and just able to balance on crutches, but even then Michael was remarkable for his expression of cheerfulness and courage.

Treatment and training did much to improve Michael's chances in life. He left St Vincent's in 1920 and set up a flourishing splint-making business in the north, returning in 1929 to manage the department. Michael Quinn trained many new boys over the next 10 years, until his death on 4 July 1939.

Above left: Children learning outside.

Above right: A hut is transformed from ward to classroom.

Monica Clarke, a retired St Vincent's orthopaedic nurse, recalls her first introduction to the Home when it was based in Clapham was through Edmund (Ted) Dunne, a young lad with tuberculosis of the hip. They had met socially and had become childhood friends.

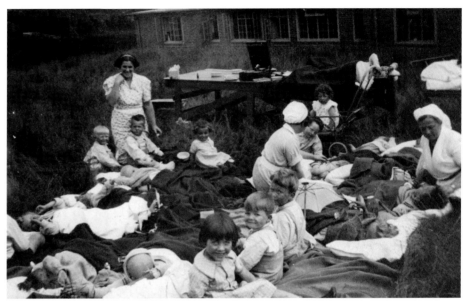

Above left: Picnic in the woods; note the bed/wheelchairs.

Above right: Everyone joining in.

Left: Day trip to the Royal Tournament, Olympia, London, in the charabanc.

Below left: Sr Teresa Fraser and Robert Jones FRCS at the front entrance to St Vincent's.

Below right: Wooden huts, 1912, south-facing towards Harrow.

Above left: Sr Magdalen on the lawn with the boys.

Above right: Sr Teresa Fraser DC and the 'old boys'.

Left: Extract from the School Register, dated 1912.

29

A holiday has been granted.

Sr Josephine.

Feb. 10th

The weather conditions still remaining very severe the children are unable to attend the schoolroom. A change has been made in the time table and in the time of teaching.

Sr. Josephine.

Feb. 18th.

Children unable to attend schoolroom today on account of snow storm. Instruction given in bed. A change made in the hours of teaching.

Sr. Josephine.

March 3rd.

Miss Killen left on Friday Feb. 28th to take up duties in Colchester. Miss Gerald from Dundee

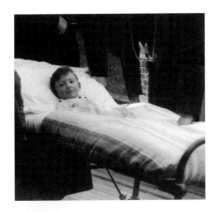

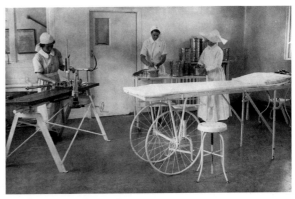

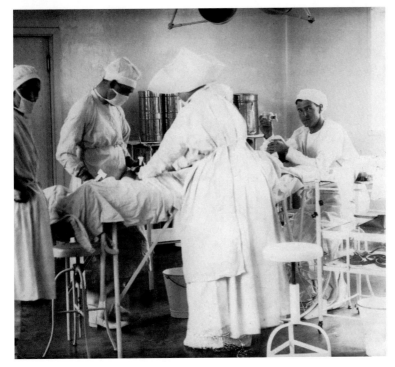

Above left: Mickey Allen on St Paul's Ward, *c.*1914.

Above right: Operating theatre, 1922. This is one of two rooms that had four walls.

Mr Brockman and Dr Thompson in theatre. In 1914 an operating theatre had been built and the first X-ray apparatus in the area was installed.

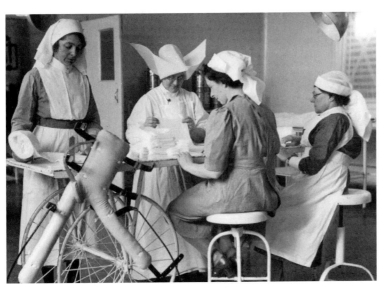

Sr Francis DC prepping in theatre.

Above: Altar boys and Fr Pat O'Daly.

Left: Musical afternoon.

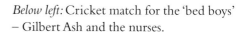

Below left: Cricket match for the 'bed boys' – Gilbert Ash and the nurses.

Below right: Outside the workshop in the 1930s.

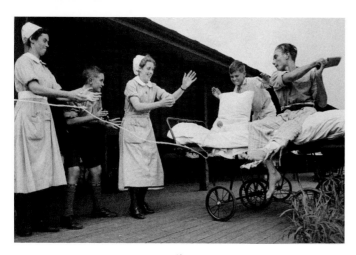

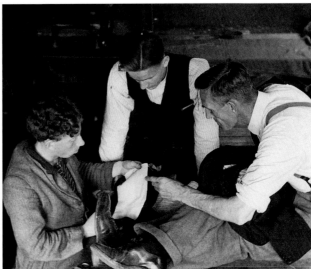

Above left: Splint-making in the St Vincent's workshop.

Above right: Mr Hagan and two young lads learning a trade in the workshop.

As his Home was close to my Convent of Notre Dame in Clapham we became friends. Ted was one of the lads transferred to Eastcote and later introduced me to Tom Clarke, who was to become my husband. Tom had been sent from Middlesborough as a four-year-old with polio after some nuns from his parish had informed his parents of St Vincent's and they were desperate to provide the best for their little boy.

Tom had the happiest memories of St Vincent's and, although some of the treatments meant painful operations, there were plenty of diversions.

These included football, cricket, billiards, table tennis and nice books to read, while Tom especially enjoyed observing the birds and wildlife. Boys also had to do hard chores such as cleaning, polishing and kitchen work. At Christmas time making decorations and building lovely cribs were especially fun, as were being in the choir and involvement in Chapel services.

Most of all was the great comradeship – the boys became like brothers.

Ted returned in 1918 to work at St Vincent's.

In 1929 Tom aged 15 years was allowed home to Middlesbrough but missed his pals and the country life, plus proving impossible for a disabled lad to get a job, he was allowed back to St Vincent's. As an employee he trained boys in splint making, leather work, boot repairs and tailoring, while also helping with the chickens.

Around 1931 Tom left St Vincent's to work outside, yet the close bond between the 'Old Boys' remained and they would visit at weekends or in the evenings.

Monica continues,

> My memories are from wartime St Vincent's in 1942 when I was called up to become a trainee orthopaedic nurse.
>
> The boys' wards had become adult wards caring for men from the forces as well as injured and sick civilians. Heavy blackout curtains were hung to be pulled across in the evening as these were 'open' wards. Walking in the grounds at night was rather nerve racking, as we had torches but batteries were limited. We had great fun, though, and I used to meet Tom, Ted and their friend Henry Holland, who later became a businessman in Northwood, walking in the grounds and on Haste Hill.
>
> Tom and I were married in 1945 and a few years later my colleague Jill married Henry.
>
> I returned as a part-time nurse when my children were settled at school. St Paul's was a boys' ward again but no longer for TB or polio, but children with brain damage, spastic deformities, spina bifida, displaced hips and congenital deformities.
>
> I had a happy 10 years working with dear Miss Kenna, Miss Byrne and Matron Sr Angela Murray DC, who had been my tutor in 1942–1945.
>
> Ted died in 1957, Henry and my husband Tom in 1991. They are together in Northwood Cemetery. Three pals united in death – we like to think of them walking together as they did on Haste Hill.

Far left: Matron Sr Angela Murray DC and a young lad called Johnnie.

Centre left: Johnnie in his wheelchair.

Centre right: Adrian, one of the lads.

Far right: Sr Jane Heery DC going for a stroll in the fresh air.

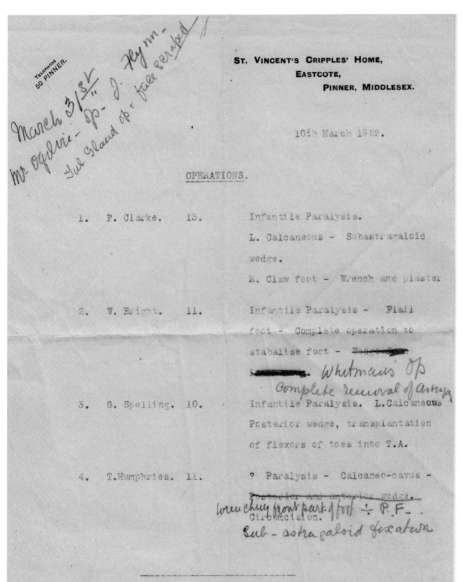

ST. VINCENT'S CRIPPLES' HOME,
EASTCOTE,
PINNER, MIDDLESEX.

Telephone 50 Pinner.

March 31st — Mr Ogilvie — op. J. Flynn — Tet Gland op — free scraped

10th March 1922.

OPERATIONS.

1. F. Clarke.   13.   Infantile Paralysis.
                         L. Calcaneous - Subastragaloid
                         wedge.
                         R. Claw foot - Wrench and plaster

2. W. Bright.   11.   Infantile Paralysis - Flail
                         foot - Complete operation to
                         stabilise foot - ~~Wedge~~
                         ~~—~~ *Whitman's Op*
                         Complete removal of Astraga

3. G. Spelling. 10.   Infantile Paralysis. L.Calcaneus
                         Posterior wedge, transplantation
                         of flexors of toes into T.A.

4. T.Humphries. 11.   ? Paralysis - Calcaneo-cavus -
                         ~~Posterior and anterior wedge.~~
                         Wrenching front part of foot + P.F.
                         Circumcision.
                         Sub - astragaloid fixation

Above left: Going for a walk.

Above centre: St Vincent's in wartime. Sr Angela Simpson (Spanish Sister) and the children.

Above right: One of the Spanish DC Sisters in England to learn English and a young girl who worked at the hospital.

Left: Surgical operating theatre list, 1922.

— FOCUS ON SURGERY —

By the 1920s operating lists were developed, along with the innovation and development of orthopaedics as a surgical speciality. This list indicates the struggle some children had in managing spastic paraplegia.

1921 THEATRE LIST

Age	Diagnosis	Surgery
9		Circumcision
14		Circumcision
16		Circumcision
13	Infantile paralysis	Calcaneum fixation (foot)
11	Infantile paralysis	Left flail foot fixation
16	Infantile hemiplegia	Division of tight muscles (leg)
10	TB spine	Excision of wedge (spine)
10	Infantile paralysis flail foot	Bridge cuboid bone (foot)
15	Infantile paralysis talipes	Wedge surgery (foot)

Above left: St Vincent's Cripples' Home Register of Operations.

Above right: Warm Ward, which was only used for recovery from the anaesthetic after surgery.

Left: Boys outside one of the huts.

Above left and centre: Miss Hopper, radiographer, and the portable X-ray machine.

Above right: Sr Francis Bailey DC, radiographer.

Below: Aerial view of the hospital.

An aptly named 'Warm Ward', one of the few rooms with four walls, adjoined the theatre for a period of recovery. The X-ray equipment had been installed in 1914 and now facilities were placed at the disposal of local hospitals to allow wounded soldiers to be X-rayed without the fatiguing journey to London, where the next nearest available machine was.

At least two of the past patients of the hospital, admitted as incurable cripples, were known to be on active service in the army in the First World War.

By 1912 the work had firmly established St Vincent's as a centre for orthopaedic treatment and rehabilitation. The average annual cost per patient rose to £38. The number of beds was increased from 23 beds to 114 in 1913.

It is interesting to note that St Vincent's was the second orthopaedic hospital founded in the country. The first was the Robert Jones and Agnes Hunt Orthopaedic Hospital, Oswestry, Shropshire. By 1922 the Royal National Orthopaedic Hospital had opened a country branch in Stanmore, Middlesex.

In 1914 a further 6 acres were purchased on the opposite side of what was then Wood Lane, earmarked to accommodate crippled girls, but the war stopped that development for some years. The site also contained a house which became the residence for the Chaplain.

Left: The nursing staff.

Below left: Young lad.

Below right: Learning to type – no fingers.

Above: A short trip to London in the charabanc.

Right: Sr Gabriel Lynch DC and children.

Below: Sr Francis Bailey DC and children having lessons.

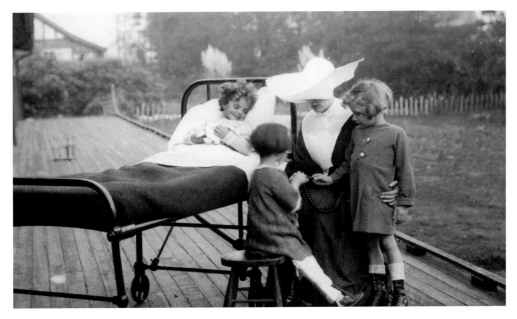

Although the building of the girls' wards was postponed, the war did not stem the flow of toys, games, food and gramophone records that were donated in abundance by local firms and individuals. The Special Constables from Northwood provided entertainments for the boys throughout the year and with presents for each child at Christmas.

The experience gained by the medical and nursing staff in orthopaedic treatment, which was something quite new, had the double effect of speeding recovery for the boys while also making space much sooner for new patients.

Children were now being accepted from all counties of England, Wales, Scotland and the Channel Islands. Treatment was paid for by county councils, boards of guardians and various other authorities, private individuals and organisations. At this time St Vincent's was also registered as a special school with the Ministry of Education, so that the education of patients was not neglected. A schoolroom was built and in addition to the basic subjects the boys were taught shorthand and typing. Inspectors from the Board of Education visited the Home and submitted favourable reports. The cost per patient had risen to £50 per year, which was less than £1 per week.

1916 saw a deficit of over £150 in the annual accounts, but this did not inhibit the enthusiasm. By 1917 the trading deficit increased to £348, so the weekly cost per patient was increased to £1 2s 6d.

The financial strain of the war years was greatly offset by the part-proceeds of a special matinee at the Drury Lane Theatre arranged by the local division of the Metropolitan Special Constabulary. The Special Constables from Northwood were praised with particular gratitude for their many evenings of entertainment, and for collecting and donating a substantial sum to the Home. It was noted that St Vincent's had served as a model for other similar institutions which had started in various parts of the country.

Gene Mahoney reflected on his childhood memories of life at St Vincent's in 1917, when he was aged seven, recalling how he and his guardian were met at Eastcote Station one summer's evening with a pony and trap.

The long winding road to the Home seemed to have no ending, then a welcome at the 'glasshouse', by a kindly Sister who ushered me into the big kitchen for some supper. When taken to the Holy Child Ward I was amazed that it had no doors and was open to all the elements.

It was fair to say my first night was not very restful, as I kept imagining all kinds of animals and prowlers walking about. We were under the care of a kindly soul known to us simply as 'Mother', who certainly lived up to her name.

OCTOBER 24, 1916

SCHOOL REGISTER LOG BOOK NO: 29547 MIDDLESEX EDUCATION AUTHORITY

A number of children are going to London this afternoon to see the picture of 'The Battle of the Somme'. For this reason a general half holiday has been given. A change in the times of the morning instruction in the sheds has been made to enable some of those children to attend the pictures.

Entry written by Sr Josephine

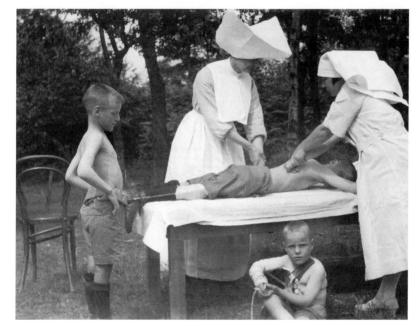

Above left:
St Vincent's
nurses and
babes in arms.

Above right:
Sr Elizabeth
Armstrong DC
and young lads.

Left: Sr
Magdalen DC
– physiotherapy
in the grounds.

Sports Day – Sr
Teresa Fraser
DC, Sr Angela
DC and Sister
Angela's sister.

Above: Sr Josephine O'Neill DC and children at a grotto within the grounds.

Left: Young lad relaxing in the garden.

The Great War was in progress but happily its significance was lost to us youngsters although one abiding memory is that of Mr McCrae Aitken making his periodic visits in full military uniform.

In the audience of the concert given by the special constables were wounded heroes in their symbolic uniform of blue and I was proud as punch when one of them gave me some cigarette cards.

Gene Mahoney recalls 'the careful guidance of Sister Josephine while preparing me for my first Holy Communion, which took place in the old Chapel'. Sr Josephine later became a senior tutor at the Hammersmith Hospital.

Gene also remembers, 'Whenever I see haymaking in progress I picture myself back in Eastcote once again on top of a haycart where an indulgent farmer had suffered me for a brief ride.'

During the Great War many existing railway lines nationwide were taken over by the Government in an effort to make the best use of services for transport of goods, armaments, service personnel, civilian travellers and also for ambulance trains. The vast majority of casualties from abroad arrived in the United Kingdom at either Dover or Southampton and, if they were not to remain in one of those two towns they were then transported onwards by train to all parts of the British mainland.

There were 200 'stopping stations' – railway stations that received sick and wounded men and women for onward transfer to local hospitals by motor car or ambulance.

Early in the conflict, a group of regional railway companies donated 12 ambulance trains to the army medical services and very soon they were carrying patients from Southampton and Dover to different parts of the UK. As the home-bound casualties mounted, four emergency trains made up of corridor coaches and dining cars came into service to accommodate 'sitting' patients. In addition, a number of North-Eastern Railway Company vans were fitted out for ambulance use and coupled to ordinary passenger trains.

The wounded from the Western Front and elsewhere were carried by hospital ships to the UK. While still at sea the ship would cable information ahead of the various categories of patients it had onboard and its estimated time of arrival at port. Each patient had been labelled with details of his wound and another label was marked with one of five areas in Britain nearest his home.

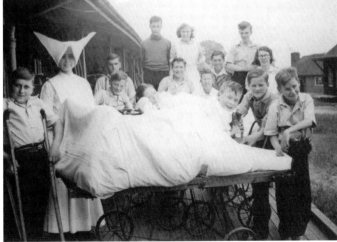

Above left: Children on the move.

Above right: Happy children.

If a man was seriously injured a plain red label was also attached to him, indicating that he required 'special consideration'. Before disembarkation from the ships began, huge 'reception sheds on the quayside were lit and heated'. Beyond the sheds the ambulance trains waited.

Patients were entrained from medical units scattered over a large area where their wounds had only received emergency treatment. On the train to the base, they received proper medical attention. This continued at the base hospital and on the hospital ships that carried them home. Consequently, when they arrived at home ports most casualties were already in a reasonably stable condition.

The soldiers continued their journey in land ambulances and arrived in the local hospitals all over London, including Mount Vernon and St Vincent's.

FEBRUARY 18, 1919

SCHOOL REGISTER LOG BOOK NO: 29547 MIDDLESEX EDUCATION AUTHORITY

Children unable to attend schoolroom today on account of snowstorm. Instruction given in bed. A change made in the hours of teaching.

Entry written by Sr Josephine

MAY 28, 1923

SCHOOL REGISTER LOG BOOK NO: 29547 MIDDLESEX EDUCATION AUTHORITY

School closed on May 21/22nd for Whitsun holidays.

Returned to school today after an absence of two weeks through illness. During this time all boys over 14 years in Class I attended trades all day. On Empire Day May 24th the King's and Queen's speeches were delivered to the children through the gramophone.

Entry written by Sr Josephine

Canon Reginald
Fellowes, Chaplain.

OCTOBER 10, 1923

SCHOOL REGISTER LOG BOOK NO: 29547 MIDDLESEX EDUCATION AUTHORITY

RELIGIOUS REPORT

Great care is taken over the instruction of these boys and the results of the examination were 'excellent'. The boys answered very well indeed in all subjects and said the prayers reverently and without mistake.

Entry written by Wm O'Sullivan

May God bless the children and their teachers.

Entry written by Card. Bourne

Above: Preparing to leave for Lourdes: Sr Vincent Neilan DC, Sr Jane Heery DC, Miss Kenna, Nurse Whelan, Jon Van Dongen and Pat, and Joseph Hennessy (note the labels around the boys' necks). The Daughters were not allowed to go to Lourdes.

Left: A visit to Lourdes, *c*.1925.

Above and below: Lourdes, May 1959.

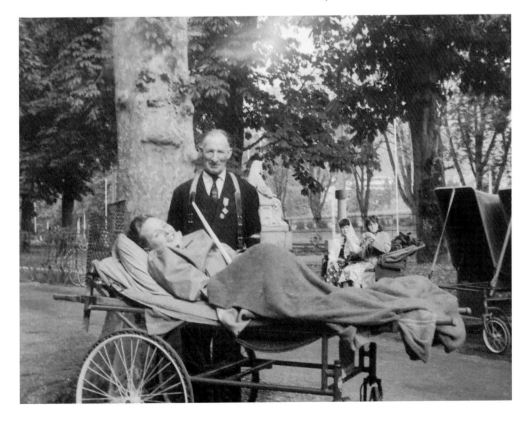

— AFTER THE GREAT WAR —

The sale of hay and pigs in 1919 realised £50, the tailoring and bootmaking workshops raised over £59 in sales, so funding a play area which was at last completed.

St Vincent's in 1919 saw the arrival of a pale, delicate boy of 14 called Raoul John Hook, from a remote Norfolk village, very shy and desperately homesick for his mother, to whom he was passionately devoted. She, poor soul, was already suffering severely from a chronic complaint, from which she shortly expired, and this was the real reason for Raoul being sent to the Home.

As he had been delicate from the age of one and was already very seriously crippled, it was thought that not much could be done to improve Raoul's condition. Sad to say this proved to be the case; probably the shock of his mother's death was the cause of an acute return to the original trouble, and in 1920 he became so ill that his life was hanging in the balance for some time, and by 1925 it was simply a question of how long he could survive the many complications of his serious disease.

Left: St Vincent's gymnasium (physiotherapy).

Below: Fundraising was an important element for St Vincent's; here are some benefactors outside the glasshouse in the 1920s.

Then, quite unexpectedly, a new factor came into his life: a party from the Home was being organised to go to Lourdes. Canon R. Fellowes was the resident Chaplain at the time.

Raoul's desire to go to Lourdes was so great and his courage so undaunted that, notwithstanding all difficulties and the very serious risk, arrangements were made for him to be sent as a stretcher case.

The result was truly marvellous; all the more perhaps, because the actual physical improvement, though very marked, was not in anyway miraculous. Raoul went full of courage, it is true, but certainly dying. He returned triumphant, and by the end of the autumn was strong enough to start getting about on crutches.

From then on Raoul made the pilgrimage to Lourdes annually, and each time he seemed filled with a new degree of courage and holiness which enabled him to overcome all physical sufferings.

His hip never improved and every surgeon who saw Raoul marvelled that he was able to leave his bed. He was never idle, and he became so proficient at splint padding that before long he was able to take complete charge of that department.

Out of working hours his many interests, varied hobbies and his telling sense of humour added zest not only to his life but also to that of his companions. Raoul John Hook died in 1936 and certainly left his mark on St Vincent's – a testimony to the great care and devotion at the Home and the mystery of Lourdes.

— ROARING INTO THE 1920S —

With the end of the war some of the long-deferred building projects began to take shape. In 1921 work at last started on the Chapel. It was to be a gift from the Order of the Daughters of Charity and was opened for use the following year.

Fr Heditch, the Chaplain from 1923 until 1935, used to accompany Canon Sutcliffe to examine the boys for the school catechism examination – he spent many hours making and repairing rosary beads. He was also a keen cyclist: he would cycle from London to Eastcote, Pinner, Ruislip and other local places for a day's outing, for he loved the country. He was also a very good cricketer and many a gallant red has been hit out of sight through his prowess as a batsman.

He was a keen supporter of the Old Boys' Association and would often offer his advice and helpful suggestions.

A physiotherapy department, added in 1923, was financed by an anonymous donation and cost £2,500; a ward which opened in 1967 cost £67,000.

In 1924 a tailor's shop opened in Northwood High Street, manned part-time by the older boys, and by 1925 it was open full-time and entirely self-supporting.

The Second Generation:
1924—1944

— Wards, 1924 – Girls —

A ward for 20 girls was opened in 1924 and St Margaret's Ward, for a further 25, was opened in 1930. Babies, boys and girls were now being admitted and often stayed for months or even years.

October 31, 1924

School Register Log Book No: 29547 Middlesex Education Authority

This afternoon sixteen of our boys are to attend a demonstration of Orthopaedic Surgery given by our surgeon Mr Olgivie at West Hampstead General Hospital. They will be accompanied by our Medical Officer and a Nursing Sister.

This afternoon the school closes for the mid term holiday. It will re open on Wednesday Nov 5th 1924.

Entry written by Sr Josephine

October 19, 1925

School Register Log Book No: 29547 Middlesex Education Authority

School work commenced in the Girls' Ward today. Miss Hill is in charge of class here and Classes IV and V (Boys) are in the charge of Miss Enright who has returned.

Entry written by Sr Josephine

Left: Girls playing.

Below: Sr Vincent and girls.

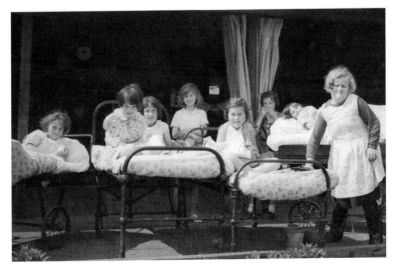

Above: St Margaret's Ward.

Left: First girls, all ages, 1924.

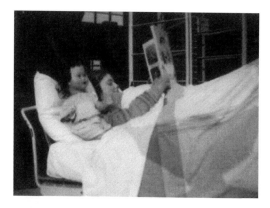

Dolly and me.

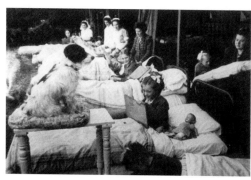

Left: Girls' ward – 'life art'.

Below: Little girl and her budgie.

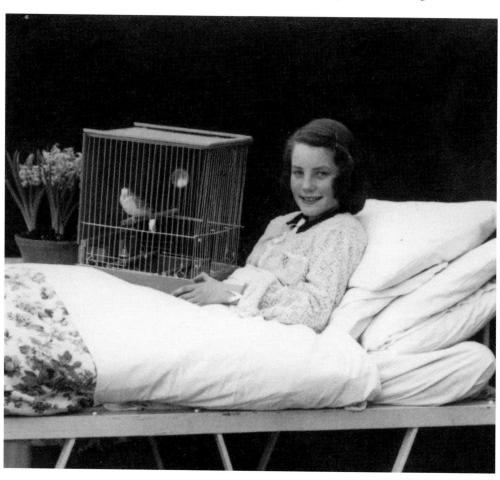

First Holy Communion, Fr Pat O'Daly.

JULY 7, 1928

SCHOOL REGISTER LOG BOOK NO: 29547 MIDDLESEX EDUCATION AUTHORITY

Being the Feast of Corpus Christi the Hospital Classes are on holiday today. The forty boys leave for the seaside to-morrow and are having school today.

Entry written by Sr Josephine

– SCOUTING AT ST VINCENT'S –

The 4th Northwood Scout Troop was formed in 1926 exclusively for boys resident at St Vincent's.

Charlie Hutchins was a well-known figure at the hospital, first as a schoolboy in 1925, then as an assistant to Mr Carey the head gardener and later the main support of St Roch's Ward. Charlie loved the country life and was filled with sorrow when the 'wicked' white pony called Sammy died as, while he used to kick and bite all within reach, he followed Charlie around like a dog.

In the early days of scouting at the Home, Charlie showed his best and there was something in the scouting appeal to 'Truth and Honour' that chimed with Charlie's deep-seated principle of what was right. It is recalled that at an early Scout meeting he was seen to turn sadly away, remarking that a 'chap with one hand could not tie knots'. However, it was not long before Charlie had mastered a great deal more than tying knots.

Above and left: Corpus Christi procession. Corpus Christi was a big feast with three Benedictions: one in the Chapel and two outside.

CUBS

A Wolf Pack was started in December 1929 and consists of 18 Cubs under the charge of Miss Denny ACM and great keenness has been shown by all Cubs.

In March 1930 the Scout Troop celebrated the third anniversary of its formation. Within a few months of the Scouts forming the Girl Guides also started.

During 1933 the Scout Troop, helped by the hospital maintenance department, constructed their own headquarters in the corner of the field at the bottom of the hill.

Above: Some Scouts standing by the hospital car outside the 'glass house' at Dolly and Jack's wedding. Harry Errington (second on left) became a cleaner for the Men's Home.

Left: Dolly and Jack on their wedding day outside the 'glass house'.

GIRL GUIDES AND BROWNIES

1st Eastcote Extension Company – there are now 12 Guides in the company and 8 Brownies and during the year 11 recruits were noted and 12 leavers on discharge from hospital.

The Brownie Pack started in November 1929.

The Guides, under the support and guidance of Miss Gilliatt, worked hard for the second-class badge and recruited for the Tenderfoot badge. The company also took part in a divisional rally at Northwood.

The Brownies were given a party at Christmas by Miss Warrender, Mrs Newth and Mrs Logsdail. At the time there were 22 Brownies, with Brown Owl being Miss Moorehouse.

All of these children must have indeed been proud of their newfound freedom – freedom which only the loving care of the Sisters of Charity could give.

Left: Kitty with the 'up boys'.

Below: 4th Northwood Troop camping in Pinner, 1926. While they were all crippled to a greater or lesser extent, it did not prevent them from camping out.

Above left: All ages took part in the fun and frolics.

Above right: Kitty Clarke with the Cubs.

NOVEMBER 10, 1926

SCHOOL REGISTER LOG BOOK NO: 29547 MIDDLESEX EDUCATION AUTHORITY

On account of our Bazaar, which takes place in London next week, we are spending the last three days of this week in preparing goods for it. Older boys, who do not take hand work, will attend trade shops.

Entry written by Sr Josephine

The Scout Troop was divided into two parties: the 'bed boys' and the 'up boys'. The change was to give the 'up boys' more activities and to do more scouting in the hut. When the boys in bed were able to get up they would, of course, join the 'up boys'.

The District-Wide Games were also held at St Vincent's in September 1946 and the camp fire was set up in front of St Michael's. John Linnel, Scout Master, was presented with the Certificate of Merit by the County Commissioner.

The following boys left the Troop through being discharged from hospital: John O'Dea, Derek Williams, Edward Corley, Charles Britnell, Ronald Willers, Alfred Hollick, Allan Hardwicke, Peter Smith, John Oakes, Reggie Wyness, Edward Maxey, Bernard Wright, Bernard Moger, David Clapinson, George Dixon, Henry Putman, Ronald Covill, Charles Cornish, Hugh Johnson, Fred Metherell, Michael Taylor, Peter White, David Sharpe, Albert Taylor, Maurice Rayment and Edward Burrett. Kevin Parker left to find employment in Torquay.

Girl Guides, Brownies, Scouts and Cubs outside their hut.

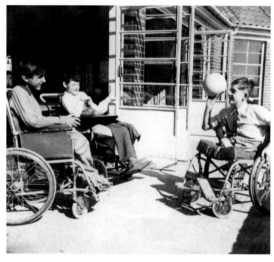

Left: Playing ball.

Below: The 'up boys' were joined by the 'bed boys', 1926.

The following are some who joined that year: James Lewis, James Regan, Pat Cannon, George Saunders, David Saunders, Alan Bulmer, Leonard Walsh, George McCarthy, Ronald Pigden.

The Girl Guides increased in quality if not in quantity, with three girls achieving second-class badges and one Guide well on her way to gaining her first-class badge.

Mr F. Corballis, a member of the Board of Management for many years, was particularly interested in the scouting movement and was one of the Chief Scout's Commissioners. He formed the first patrol and maintained an interest in the St Vincent's Scouts until he died in 1934.

The Scouts' hut was officially opened in 1934 by Mr Hubert Martin, International Commissioner, and also present was Sir Cecil Pereira and Major Waley. The number of Scouts at this time was 21.

In 1945 the Captain of Girl Guides recalled:

When Sister Mary (Matron) asked me to re-form St Vincent's Guide Company, I grudgingly agreed to do some thinking, with a sinking heart, of my remaining leisure hours fleeting fast away. However, on broaching the subject on St Margaret's Ward 'big girls', my proposal was greeted with such a clamour of delight and enthusiasm that I felt ashamed of my first hesitation, immediately became thoroughly interested, and enlisted ten recruits on the spot, some of whom were already enrolled Guides. No one was left out who was solid enough to join.

Our immediate problem was to equip each Guide with a uniform, and with the help of Bettie Beattie, our only 'up girl', I managed to unearth five tunics. Thus half the company provided for. Another five had to be obtained by hook or by crook. To buy more required cherished coupons! We decided to 'borrow' some Brownie uniforms, dye them navy blue, and risk the ire of some Brown Owl! Ties, too, were a problem, but Sister Mary very kindly came to the rescue with some white material which also could be dyed.

I'm afraid I was a trifle optimistic over my dyeing ability. The required shade for ties is saxe blue. In the process of dyeing everything for a radius of several yards became this beautiful colour excepting, of course, the ties, which took on a mottled, greenish-greyish hue! My efforts at dyeing the Brownie tunics were no more successful. In endeavouring to change three of them to navy blue, I produced one black, one dark-brown and the other refused altogether to desert its fellow Brownies! There will have to be another session with the dye pot at some future date, when we hope for better results. In the meantime we must remember the Guide Law which says 'A Guide smiles and sings under all difficulties'.

In spite of many set-backs, we have now succeeded in forming a Company consisting of two Patrols, the Forget–me-nots and Scarlet Pimpernel. The Patrol Leaders are Dorothy Milsom, who contributed ably to the last issue of this magazine the *BedPost*, and Gerda Schonbrunn, with Gillian Morgan and Marion McKernan as their respective seconds.

Mrs Windle, our District Commissioner, very kindly offered to be present at our first meeting, and has subsequently been of great assistance to me in this new venture. She gave a very nice little talk on Guiding in general, after which everyone felt a little more intelligent.

CAPTAIN

Scouts 4th Northwood Scout Troop News, 1945

Bill Quinn reported activity in 1945:

The Scouts have been doing the routine jobs of scouting efficiently and cheerfully. Besides badge work and the usual tests, we do tracking, mapping, camping, games, general knowledge tests, and a host of other things. We propose doing a pantomime which the bed boys will be able to take part. We hope to have our usual Christmas Party. The County Commissioner visited us recently, and spoke highly of the spirit and work of the Troop.

On 22 September we had wide games. A camp fire and sing-song followed, and about 230 scouts took part.

A dance in aid of the Troop funds was held in Hesdin Hall, Ruislip on 6 October. A sum of £12 was obtained.

Patrol Leader Ken Mason has passed his Public Health and got his green and yellow cords. M. Harrison has got his bookbinding.

F. Metherell, L. Nixon, D. Sharpe and E. Corley have left us. We wish them good luck. We welcome M. Harrison and J. Smith back and J. O'Dea, who is new.

Skipper and Bill went to the Rover Moot at Caxton Hall, which was addressed by the County President Sir Alfred Pickford, who introduced the Chief Scout, Lord Rowallan. After tea, the Chief chatted with us all. We would like to give a big welcome to the revived Guide Troop, and to assure them that we shall do everything we can to help them.

Bill Quinn (1945)

The Scouts' and Guides' activities were suspended during the war and they had their first Christmas party since the company reopened in January 1946. Division Commissioners Mrs Newth and Mrs Windle, helped by a number of Guides of the 2nd Ruislip Company, were on hand to make the party a great deal of fun.

Scouts outside their Scout Hut. The Troop was started up in 1926 by Jack Carr (Scout Leader) and Kitty Clarke.

The entertainment included two performances where the children made their own costumes: 'The King's Breakfast' by A.A. Milne and 'The Raggle Taggle Gypsies O'.

On 29 June 1946 the Scouts joined the Middlesex County Scout Rally and six from the troop took part in the finale. A visiting Scout Master from Turkey came to explore how St Vincent's was managing handicapped scouting, with the intention of starting a similar scheme in Turkey.

— CRICKET 11S AT ST VINCENT'S —

Those boys with leg defects did all the batting, while those whose legs were good did all the running. The boys in the Junior 11 are made up as follows: three are convalescent from TB hip, one from TB spine, six from infantile paralysis and one from scoliosis.

JUNE 23, 1927

SCHOOL REGISTER LOG BOOK NO: 29547 MIDDLESEX EDUCATION AUTHORITY

School boys' cricket team granted permission to leave at 3pm in order to play cricket match at Northwood.

Entry written by Sr Josephine

For those who were bedridden, an inter-bed match was devised. As treatment continued to improve and the time spent in hospital shortened, the junior sports teams slowly faded into memory.

In 1927 new workshops were built, resulting in the bootmaking, tailoring, splint-making and leatherworking activities being housed under one roof.

The Chaplain's house was extended to provide a flat for a doctor, which was further extended subsequently for a second doctor and a parking space for the Sisters' car much later in the 1950s.

– EDUCATION AT ST VINCENT'S –

St Vincent's was also registered with the then Ministry of Education as a Special School, so that the patients' general education was not neglected.

1930 GOVERNMENT CERTIFICATES

The Home was certified as a school by the Board of Education under 62 and 63 Vict. c. 32, and by the Home Office. It was approved under the National Insurance Act 1911, by the Ministry of Health, as a sanatorium for children suffering from Surgical Tuberculosis.

Cases Eligible: Children suffering from every form of orthopaedic diseases, including tubercular and other joint diseases, infantile paralysis, etc. Children who are mentally deficient or suffering from phthisis or fits cannot be admitted.

1930 APPLICATION FOR ADMISSION AND TERMS

A printed form of application had to be filled out and forwarded to the Matron, together with the special Medical Certificate attached, duly signed by a qualified medical practitioner after examination of the applicant. Personal applications for admission could be made at any of the clinics.

The sum which Public Assistance Committees, and other societies were charged in respect of maintenance, clothing, education and surgical treatment of crippled children of school age, was £75 10s per annum, but for those retained beyond the end of the school term in which they attain the age of 16 years the annual charge would be increased to £100.

Above: St Vincent's cricket team.

Below: Cricket 11, 1925.

St. Vincent's Orthopaedic Hospital,

Eastcote, Pinner,

Middlesex.

January, 1926.

ACCOUNTS FOR YEAR ENDED DECEMBER 31ST, 1925.

Receipts.		Expenditure.	
Hospital Sisters	£220. 0. 0.	Clothing, Board and Furniture	£168. 6. 4.
School Sister	£359.18. 0.	Retreats and Travelling	£ 65. 7. 3.
Total -	£579.18. 0.	Medicine and Dentist	£ 8.17. 9.
(£100) Interest paid on £2,000, and petty cash			£281.15. 1.
			£524. 6. 5.

Balance - £55. 11. 7.

Above: Chaplain's home: Rev. Brown and the doctor's flat.

Left: This copy of the year-end accounts for 1926 indicates how challenging finance was, even during the early days.

Above: St Vincent's main entrance; the bell is still at St Vincent's.

Left: School time.

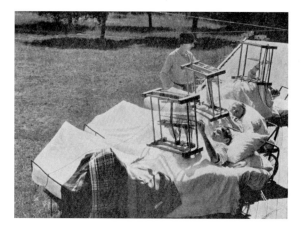

Roller handlooms, keeping the children very busy.

Left: Foot-powered loom operated by the girls.

Below: A model of the schoolroom and ward.

In the case of children sent by County or Borough Councils under a scheme for the institutional treatment of tuberculosis or by Education Authorities, the charge was a rate of £100 per annum, as no grants of any kind were received by the Board of Management of the hospital from the Board of Education in respect of such children. No additional charge was made for surgical instruments supplied.

In January 1934, the Special School was inspected by H.M. Inspector Dr M. Bywaters. She expressed herself to be very satisfied with the standard reached, and with the lines on which the school was being conducted.

Weaving had been added to the handwork syllabus. Besides small roller looms, a foot-powered loom had been acquired. Special attention had been paid as usual to plain needlework, elementary dressmaking, and stitchcraft generally in the workroom available to the older girls.

Jim Laffey was admitted to St Vincent's with infantile paralysis in 1930 when he was 11 years old. Jim reflects on his happy times as a patient, staff member and a very active 'Old Boy', contributing to *The Link* magazine on many occasions. Jim goes on to point out that in 1926 the first wards were built for girls:

> Pardon me if I digress for a moment, but the word 'ward' brings a chuckle. They were affectionately known as the 'sheds'. Picture the scene. A wooden building about 100 feet long with a back, two ends and a roof, with a dressing room, sluice, bathroom and toilet and kitchen tacked on to the back, but the front gaping wide to the elements. There was the luxury of halfway down canvas curtains but they were only drawn if it was raining or snowing HEAVILY and only if the rain or snow was blowing into the 'shed'.
>
> Not a vestige of heating of any sort (except a coal fire in the kitchen) so if you were an 'up patient' and found it too cold, you just snuggled into bed under a mountain of blankets, and wore a pair of thick woollen gloves if you wanted to read. Yes, you had to be tough if you wanted to be a patient at St Vincent's in those days.

He remained until he retired due to ill health in 1977 then moved to the British Polio Fellowship Hostel in Newcastle, to be near his relatives. Jim was very happy at this hostel and it is sad that his time there was so short; however, he gave a great deal to St Vincent's. Jim reflects:

> I spent six years as a patient in the hospital, where I learned the rudiments of clerical work, then 36 years on the staff of the finance, salaries and wages department.
>
> I had to seek premature retirement because of the deterioration of a physical disability caused by polio and, not being able to cope with a retirement villa in the Bahamas, I had to settle for a 'pad' in the hospital, kitted out rent free by the authorities.

Boys on St Paul's Ward, 1951.

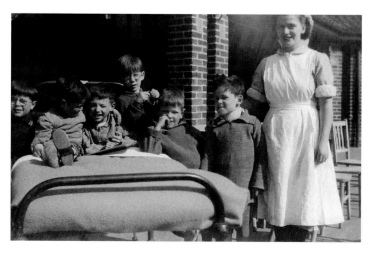

Boys on St Paul's Ward, 1951, including Ronnie, JoJo, Mickey Gordon, Tommy and John.

So with my typewriter and calculator and a fair supply of odd jobs to keep me occupied, my daily paper, a few books and a television set, I was thoroughly enjoying the relaxations of retirement.

The General Office, Board Room and the upstairs portion, which was the Nurses' Home, was the original building when St Vincent's moved onto the site, as was the house on the other side of the road, which provided flats for the resident doctors and the Chaplain.

St Vincent's Cripples' Home was its first proper title and Eastcotonians used to refer to it as the 'Cripples Home' – not something that could be said today.

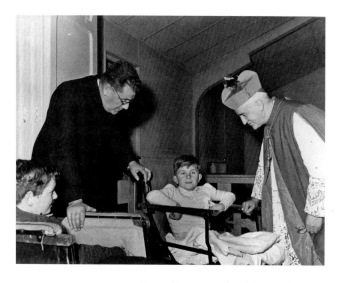

Above: Boys meeting Bishop Craven.

Right: Johnny Sheehan meets Bishop Craven with Fr O'Daly.

Bowley's Ruislip repair shop (photo permission by William Bowley).

Above left: Bill Bowley, 1938 (photo permission by William Bowley).

Above right: First shop (repairs), Station Approach, Northwood, 1918: Bill Bowley (left) and Bill Russell (photo permission by William Bowley).

Under the guidance of some of the pioneers of modern orthopaedic surgery, the late Sir Robert Jones FRCS, his protégé the late Mr David McCrae Aitken FRCS and Sr Teresa Fraser, a Daughter of Charity and the Home's first Matron, (a post she held until 1941), St Vincent's prospered and expanded.

It is worth noting that a few lads were destined to make an impact in the district. Mr Bill Bowley owned a number of shoe shops in the locality: they included Ruislip, which was situated where the bicycle shop is currently; Northwood, the current shop on the corner behind the War Memorial in the High Street; Rickmansworth, Beaconsfield and Stanmore – all of which are corner properties; and one up in Solihull.

Bill found himself as a 10-year-old lad at St Vincent's after a fall off his bicycle and developing TB of his knee. He spent a considerable time at St Vincent's having successful treatment on his leg to ensure he could still walk. During this period at St Vincent's he was offered the opportunity to learn basketwork and

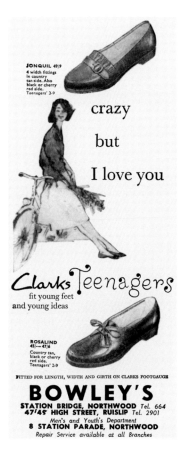

Above: Newspaper clipping advertising Bowley's shoes.

Top right: Northwood High Street in the early 1900s (photo permission by William Bowley).

Bottom right: The front window of Bowley's shoe shop (photo permission by William Bowley).

For High Class Boot and Shoe Repairs

HOLLANDS

99, Ryefield Parade
Northwood Hills.

PHONE : NORTHWOOD 2471

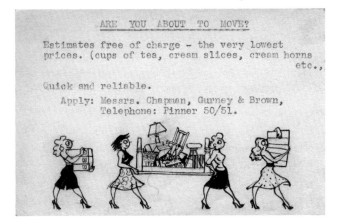

ARE YOU ABOUT TO MOVE?

Estimates free of charge – the very lowest
prices. (cups of tea, cream slices, cream horns
etc.,

Quick and reliable.

Apply: Messrs. Chapman, Gurney & Brown,
Telephone: Pinner 50/51.

Above left: Bowley's shoe shop with the War Memorial in the foreground, 1963 (photo permission by William Bowley).

Above right: Advertisement for Hollands shoe repairers.

Left: Entrepreneurial approach – 'furniture removals'.

weaving or shoe and boot repairs. The rest is, of course, history. Despite a fixed knee joint, he was very mobile.

Once he was discharged from St Vincent's he used his new skills to develop a small business which initially started as a workshop in his parents' garden shed. Bill eventually opened a shop in Northwood in the 1940s and expanded the business over the years, and his son, also Bill, with his entrepreneurial skills developed a very successful business.

They identified that the 'repair income' made up 20% of the profit and the effort required to meet the demand from challenging customers and the hassle it could cause was about 80%, so they eventually devoted the business to selling smart shoes. By 1962 they were established in Northwood. Bill Bowley's son did his own apprenticeship for three years with Clarks shoes and recalls 'that during the harsh winter of 1965 that they sold over 1,000 Wellington boots, but the spring/summer collection was going to be a challenge as people were not window shopping or thinking of the next season's designs.

Bill goes on to explain:

I became a travelling salesman meeting with regular customers at home and informing them of the new designs. I sold crocodile shoes and matching handbags for 50 guineas and some of the best clients bought the same design in different colours and the spring collection of pink and white shoes sold very well. In those days you could buy a return flight to Jersey for £15 and so when one of my 'regulars' moved I went to visit them and did a respectable trade until a local businessman opened a similar trade.

There were a number of young lads who made a good living in this trade, including Albert Case, who ran a successful shoe repair business in Northwood Hills for many years until he retired (his shop was situated on the former site of Barclays Bank).

Martin Lear, another 'Old Boy', was a partner in the leather goods firm of Lear & Gristwood in Ruislip High Street and Mr Henry Holland also had a thriving repair trade in Northwood. As already mentioned, Henry Holland was great friends with Ted Dunne and Tom Clarke and are buried near each other in Northwood Cemetery.

MARCH 9, 1931

SCHOOL REGISTER LOG BOOK NO: 29547 MIDDLESEX EDUCATION AUTHORITY

The second girls' ward 'St Teresa's' opened today for schoolwork. Miss Ashworth commenced duties in the above ward today.

Entry written by Sr Josephine

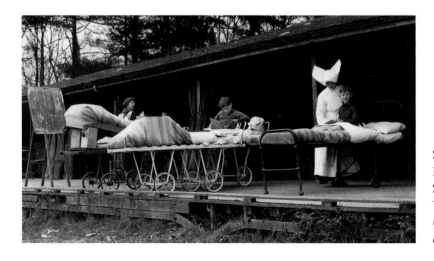

Sr Gertrude Heery DC, St Michael's Ward shed (note the easel).

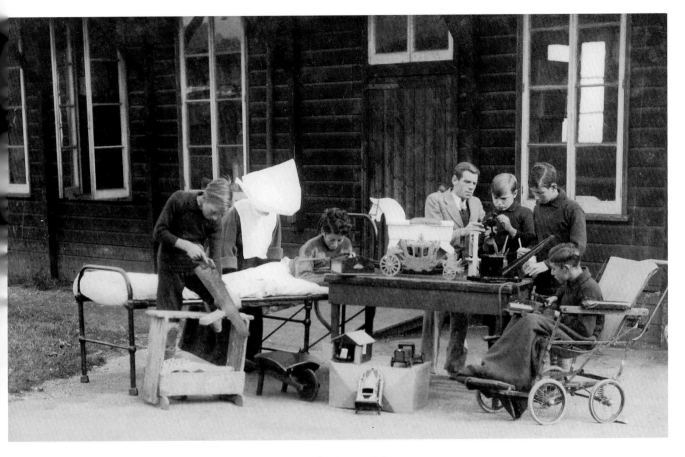

Sr Kevin DC, Mr Hagan and the boys outside the workshop.

Boot shop: Bill Clarke and Alan Chettle.

Above: Boot shop: boys learning a trade.

Below: Boys in the tailors' workshop.

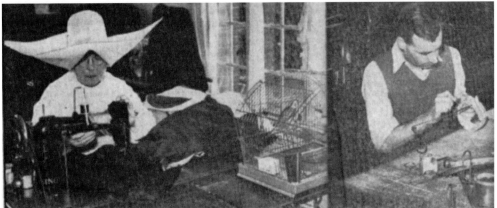

Top: Girls' workroom.

Above: Mr Richardson, making leg iron callipers, and Sr Agnes DC.

Left: Workshop.

Above: 1934 aerial photograph of St Vincent's Orthopaedic Hospital.

Below: 1934 geographical map of the area.

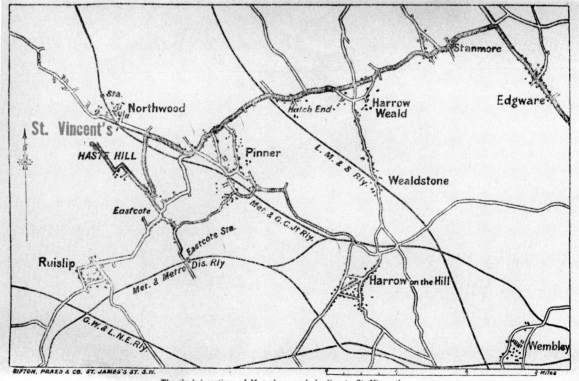

The shaded portions of Map show roads leading to St. Vincent's.

Girls playing in the open air.

By the 1930s the hospital boasted eight of these spartan wards, its bed complement was 200 and it was always full, 80% of the patients being children or young teenagers.

During 1934 plans were drawn up to replace the wooden wards with permanent brick buildings and to centralise the heating system. The first of the wooden wards were demolished in 1935, with, to quote the Matron of the day, 'the enthusiastic help of the ragamuffins on St Roch's Ward', who were scratching through the debris for any old pennies which might have fallen through the floorboards over the years. The newly built brick wards were still open on the south sides.

That year saw a new girls' ward built, this time with brick pillars but no curtains. Part of the ward included a large workroom with sewing and knitting machines where the girls could learn dressmaking, needlework, knitting and domestic economy. It was the counterpart of the boys' workshops, preparing the girls for a new life once they left the hospital.

At an international exhibition of cripples' work in Edinburgh in 1934, St Vincent's competed in the hospital schools section and came away with 24 diplomas. Later in the year 12 certificates were won at a needlecraft exhibition in London.

St Roch was a saint who lived in the 14th century and devoted all his time to the care of the sick at the time of the bubonic plague.

St Roch's Ward had been for boys who came for convalescing when their surgical treatment had finished. The 'up chaps' stayed for a while before either being sent home or to one of the workshops, where they could look forward to a weekly handout of pocket money. With the ever-increasing improvements in treatment the number of long-stay patients gradually diminished.

With them went the boys' football and cricket teams, the table tennis team, the Scouts, Guides, Brownies and Cubs. Many of the 'Old Boys' reminisced with nostalgia about the football pitches and cricket pavilion on 'thirty acres' – the playing fields.

JANUARY 1, 1934

SCHOOL REGISTER LOG BOOK NO: 29547 MIDDLESEX EDUCATION AUTHORITY

Thirteen girls accompanied by teacher attended the matinee performance of 'Peter Pan' yesterday at the Palladium, London.

Entry written by Sr Josephine

The *News Chronicle* newspaper had installed radio equipment in all the wards in 1935, which by 1953 was well worn out and was replaced.

Above: Mother General from Paris, on a visit to St Vincent's, with a little girl outside one of the wards.

Left: Sr Gabriel Lynch DC and child.

Right: St Paul's Ward: children prepare for their first Holy Communion.

Below: Fr Glavin: first Holy Communion.

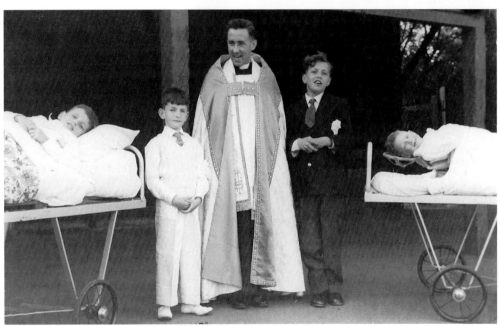

In 1932 Holy Child Ward was built for babies, containing 24 cots. The ward was open as usual on the south side, but sliding glass doors were added which could completely enclose the rear half of the ward. This half could be heated if necessary – a significant change.

MAY 16, 1935

SCHOOL REGISTER LOG BOOK NO: 29547 MIDDLESEX EDUCATION AUTHORITY

Twenty-eight boys attended by a teacher and an orderly are visiting the Royal Tournament at the Olympia this afternoon.

Entry written by Sr Josephine

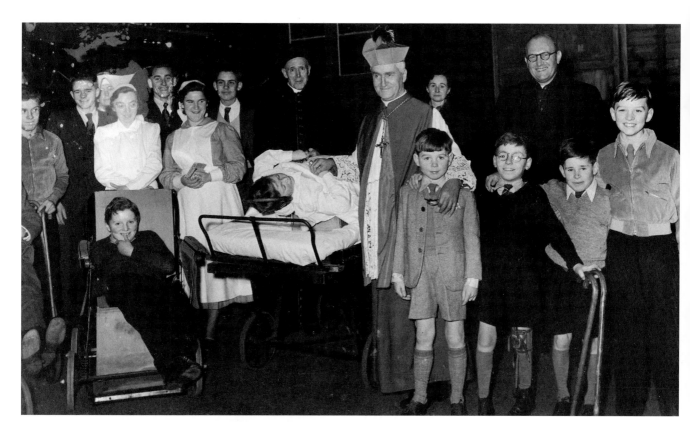

Above: Mgr Sutton and Fr O'Daly at a Confirmation.

Left: Occasionally, over the years, the hospital has produced sets of postcards for sale to patients and visitors; this one shows St Paul's Ward in *c.*1930.

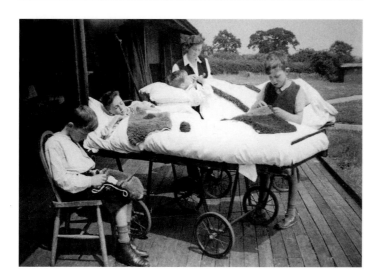

St Paul's Ward.

Holy Child
Ward: the
baby ward
(postcard).

Holy Child
Ward with
nurses and
babies.

Child Ward
(postcard).

It is interesting to note that the salary for nurses in 1933 was £18 per year, rising to £24 after six months, and they had to fund their own uniforms. Note also that horse-drawn cabs gave way to motorised transport, although the wet footpath still existed.

Many children were able to go home to their families following successful surgical and appliance treatment.

The following pictures illustrate the success and variety of conditions managed at St Vincent's.

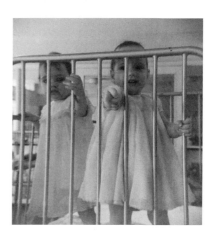

Top left: School days on St Paul's Ward, five- to six-year-olds.

Top right: Holy Child Ward: baby unit.

Above left: St Margaret's Ward for girls.

Above right: Little babies.

Right: Twin sisters.

Left: Baby unit.

Below: Aftercare clinics.

AFTER-CARE CLINICS

After-Care Centres in the London and Middlesex area where new cases can be seen and the after-care of old cases attended to are :

Central Clinic.—At St. Andrew's Hall, Carlisle Place, Westminster, S.W.1.
   1st and 3rd Tuesdays.   Surgeons : Mr. McCrae Aitken
   2.30 p.m.   1st Tuesdays.
Camden Town Clinic.—At Hampstead General Hospital Out-Patients Department, Bayham Street.
   Last Friday of each month.   Surgeon : Mr. Ogilvie.
   10.30 a.m.
Eastcote Clinic.—At St. Vincent's Hospital, Eastcote, Pinner.
   Every Wednesday.   Surgeons : Mr. McCrae Aitken
   2 p.m.   or Mr. Ogilvie.
Northwood Clinic.—At Northwood and Pinner Memorial Hospital, Pinner Road, Northwood.
   2nd Wednesday.   Surgeon : Mr. Ogilvie.
   2.30 p.m.
Ruislip Clinic.—At Church Hall, Catholic Church, High Street, Ruislip.
   1st Friday.   Surgeon : Mr. Brockman.
   2 p.m.
Bow Clinic.—At St. Vincent's Convent, 189 Devon's Road, Bow.
   3rd Thursday.   After-Care Sister.
   3 p.m.
Willesden Green Clinic.—At Our Lady's House, 247 Willesden Lane, N.W.2.
   Last Thursday of each month.   After-Care Sister.
   2.30 p.m.

Massage Department

Ruislip Massage Clinic.—At Church Hall, Catholic Church, High Street, Ruislip.
   Each Monday, Tuesday and Thursday.   3—6 p.m.
   Each Wednesday and Friday.   2—5 p.m.

HOSPITAL STATISTICS

April 1st, 1933 to March 31st, 1934

ADMISSIONS AND DISCHARGES

	Boys	Girls	Total
Admissions	91	66	157
Discharges	84	60	144
Number of Beds Available			.. 196
Average Number of Beds Occupied			.. 190
† Average Length of Stay			461.86 days

† Ascertained by dividing daily total of patients by the number of patients treated to a conclusion, and includes industrial cases.
* Temporary address during rebuilding of above :—St. Peter & St. Edward's Hall, 3 Palace St., S.W.1.

14

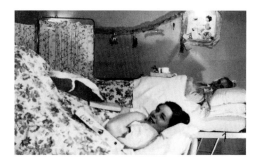

Above left: Muriel Russell on St Margaret's Ward, Christmastime.

Above right: Girls on St Margaret's Ward.

Daughters of Charity visit by Mother Superior from Paris. Note the priest's house in the background.

— FARMING AT ST VINCENT'S —

The farm was a constant source of fun, and the children made many furry friends. Extensions and improvements were made to the farm buildings in 1933. In that year 11 tons of potatoes and 31,000 eggs were produced on the farm. The farm continued to make rapid progress and later supplied 45,000 eggs, 6 tons of fruit, over 13 tons of potatoes, and many other vegetables to the hospital.

The old carpenter's workshop, which had been idle since 1927, became the headquarters of the now flourishing Old Boys' Association.

An advertisement appeared in the 1920s for the St Vincent's poultry farm, offering day-old chicks, hatching eggs and spring chicken in season. The poultry farm was the last remnant of the farming era to survive and it eventually closed in 1970.

Left: Peter Moore, one of the boys on the farm.

Below: Bacon and eggs.

Bottom left: Piglets on the farm.

Bottom right: Haymaking.

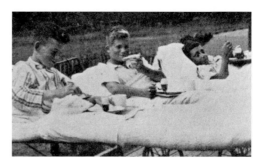

MARCH 15, 1940

SCHOOL REGISTER LOG BOOK NO: 29547 MIDDLESEX EDUCATION AUTHORITY

Miss Bywaters, Her Majesties Inspectorate (HMI), visited school today and examined all classes.

Entry written by Sr Josephine

During 1937, St Vincent's began admitting adults, as the needs of children were decreasing. By 1940 two new brick wards, still open-air but with sliding doors to cushion the patients against the slightest draught, had been built, plus a Private Patients' Wing. The original private patient's fee was £2.20 per week, but by 1977 it had risen to £35.00 per day.

Sister Teresa Matthews, whose blood sister was a Daughter of Charity, recalls her association with St Vincent's following a visit in April 2009 to be part of the support community for the Daughters of Charity residing there.

It was with a sense of rediscovering a place I'd first seen in 1952. This was when I came with my father to visit my sister, Sr Sheila Mathews (then known as Sr Bernard) who was a member of the community and staff there.

She had first come to St Vincent's in 1945 as a young sister from Ireland and she would have been 24 years old. I was 11 and I well remember how we as a family, and especially my parents, felt when the first member of the family went abroad!

Writing letters to Sheila became very important and I remember addressing letters to her at 'St Vincent's Orthopaedic Hospital, Eastcote, Pinner, Middlesex' and giving her the title of Saint Bernard!

My mother visited Sheila there with my sister Betty some time between 1945 and 1948. Betty was then working with Aer Lingus and would have been able to get good deals on airfares so they flew over and this was certainly a first for my mother.

I remember hearing my mother talking about staying in 'Ye Olde Barn' and bringing back a most beautifully embroidered tablecloth which I think had been given to Sheila by one of the patients. It was so well embroidered that the back was almost the same as the front. We had it in our home for many years.

I'm not sure which department Sheila was in at this time but she used to talk of sleeping in a sort of cabin in the woods when she was on night duty. I later heard other sisters saying the same thing. She also used to tell us that she loved to go into the woods to get logs and moss and other things to make the crib for the Chapel at Christmas.

1949 was a big year as Sheila came to Ireland for her Retreat and rest as it was called in those days. I think she had left St Vincent's by then, but she was to return there in 1951 and stayed there till 1954.

It was during this second time in St Vincent's that my father and I came to visit prior to my entering the Community of the Daughters of Charity.

We stayed in London and travelled out to Pinner on the train each day to see Sheila. I remember what looked like a Tudor house which I think must have been where the Sisters lived, judging from photos I've seen. We met Sr Mary, who was Sr Mary Neville.

As my father and I walked down the hill from St Vincent's to get the train back to London we used to sing the theme tune from *The Archers* as we felt we were in the English countryside! Of course when we were there we visited the farm. This had repercussions as foot and mouth disease was around at the time. On arriving back at Dun Laoghaire there was a large notice saying that anyone who had been on a farm in England must go and have their shoes sprayed with disinfectant. As we hadn't exactly been working on the farm I don't think it applied to us but I remember dragging my poor father to be sprayed despite his reassurances that we were exempt!!

-- POST-WAR ST VINCENT'S --

St Margaret's Ward was built for girls. Later it became St Vincent's Ward for men.

In 1933 the covered play area of St Roch's Ward was removed to make way for a small plaster room, and here you see one of the first patients in the country to be fitted with a plaster cast.

 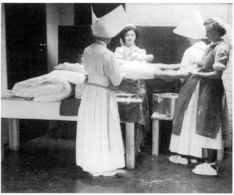

Above left: A visiting bishop at the hospital's main entrance.

Above right: Sr Catherine DC, Theatre Sister, and Sr Jane Heery DC, Plaster Sister, applying a plaster hip spica to a hip.

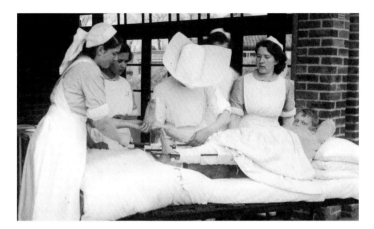

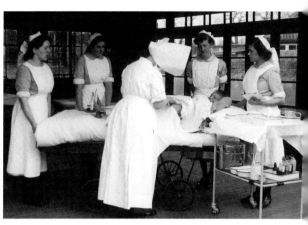

Above left: Frame technology.

Above right: Dressing technique.

Above: Cricket in the field.

Right: 'Cowboys and Indians', 1934.

How can one describe St Vincent's Hospital? It had a reputation second to none – it was a haven of tranquillity, an oasis of peace and quiet.

An anonymous donor had provided money to build an aviary in 1915. Sr Agnes Neville had budgies in her sewing room. She bred these birds and sold them at the garden fete and the local police would bring in birds to her not claimed by anyone.

The earliest laundry and ironing room formed part of the administration buildings in the main house, and once the room became vacant it was converted into a dining room for the domestic staff. The 1914 'new' laundry remained until 1934 when it was rebuilt behind the priest's house. It was again demolished in 1980 and rebuilt as part of a major building appeal.

While she was on Retreat one year her sewing room burned down. The Provincial called her in to give her the sad news! However, Sr Agnes was thrilled – she had prayed for a new department and saw this as an answer to prayer!

Mr and Mrs Miseroy with Miss Olive Bacon and Sr Mary Neville DC, Matron, opening the Garden Fete.

Sr Kevin DC and girls toy-making outside the burned-out sewing room, 1937.

Left: A bit of the Wild West.

Below, left and right: Young lads looking happy.

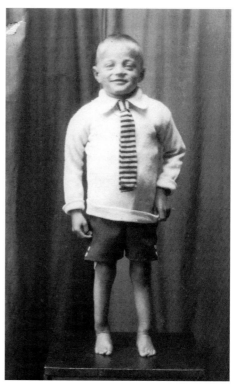

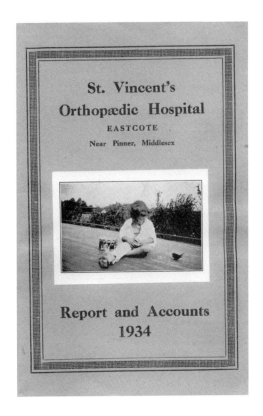

Above left: Teddy and us.

Above right: 1934 Annual Report.

1935 Annual Garden Fete showing the three-sided sheds (wards).

Cockney 'pearly king and queen', born within the sound of Bow Bells.

She planned the new sewing room and supervised its rebuilding. The uniforms and linen for the hospital were all made there. Sr Neville DC, who was the Matron, was very particular about many elements, and appearance and a professional approach was essential for the Daughters and the nurses who worked at the hospital. The nurses wore uniforms but did not like to wear them with hems too long. Whilst retaining modesty and a practicality for working within the wards, the nurses did alter their hems to be seen as partially fashionable. Sr Neville did not really approve, but there was a level of understanding and some compromise on a suitable hem length. The nurses were said to remind Sr Neville that they were not novices or religious sisters who had to wear the regulation habit to a required standard. Notwithstanding that, the nurses always looked presentable, and Sr Neville was proud of their ability to provide excellent care and look smart.

Every picture taken of the children shows happiness and joy. 'Old Boys' of the hospital, who were in for treatment decades ago talk of perfect contentment and the motherly care of the nursing sisters.

On 15 July 1934, Claridges Hotel in London hosted the jubilee banquet by the British Orthopaedic Society in aid of the foremost orthopaedic hospital in Great Britain: St Vincent's Hospital. Special guests included His Grace the Archbishop of Westminster as guest of honour, Sir James Calder, Mr McCrae Aitken and the Band of the Coldstream Guards, who played during the banquet.

The first private wards were built as an experiment in 1935 and soon proved very popular.

St Vincent's suffered a grievous loss with the death of the Cardinal Archbishop of Westminster in 1935. Cardinal Bourne had been interested in St Vincent's since its earliest days in Clapham. As one of the original Trustees he was instrumental in securing financial assistance to help build and develop the hospital when it moved to Eastcote. The Management Board were very upset when the news of his death was relayed to them.

IRISH AMBASSADOR VISITED

When the Irish Ambassador visited, Margaret White, a little girl from St Margaret's Ward, presented the bouquet to his wife. Sr Mary Jo Powell was in charge of the ward and so was guiding Margaret while she presented the flowers.

Margaret White.

Irish Ambassador and his wife meeting the boys and Miss Kenna at the horse show, 1952.

The Ambassador's wife praised St Vincent's, 'all the lovely birds and the countryside', and asked Margaret if she knew what a lark was? Margaret replied, 'Oh yes – a funny joke.' Sr Mary Jo recalls, 'I was mortified! We had practised curtseying et cetera but the girls always had jokes!'

Sr Mary Neville DC was Matron from 1942 to 1949 and was a late vocation, becoming a Daughter of Charity in her early forties. She steered St Vincent's through some challenging times. Sr Mary was very keen to have new Sisters work at St Vincent's. However, she usually gave them six weeks to settle in and become accustomed to the ways of Pinner and the cold draughty wards. If after the six weeks' 'probation' the Sister did not settle then she would be posted somewhere different as the work was hard and you needed to pull your weight.

Many changes and developments were happening on the site and in 1936 a new ward was in use. It was officially opened on 15 July 1936, in the presence of a distinguished gathering, which included His Grace the Archbishop of Westminster, Sir Cecil Pereira, Mr McCrae Aitken and Mr Potter, well known to those who had been at Clapham.

Above left: St Paul's Ward, children with toy 'doggy'.

Above right: Children playing with toy soldiers.

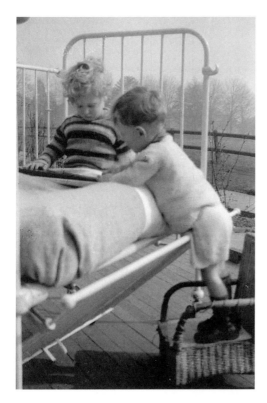

Above: Enjoying the goldfish.

Left: Sharing a story.

Below left: Plenty of friends.

Below right: Children sitting on the lawn outside their hut.

Bottom: Daughters of Charity, 1936. Matron Sr Teresa Fraser is at the centre; the remainder of the group are nurses.

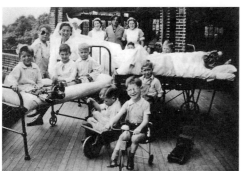

Above: Site view indicates the impact of the replacement of wooden wards with solid brick buildings.

The opening ceremony was performed by Lady Eldon. Her speech began: 'Your Grace, Sir Cecil, ladies and gentlemen. I feel it is a great honour to be asked to open this new ward, and thus be able to take part in the wonderful work which is carried out at St Vincent's Hospital.'

This beautiful ward was replacing a wooden shed which had been erected 25 years earlier for £300 and was the past home of the patients when the hospital opened. The shed had served its purpose but at the end of that time it was in danger of falling to pieces. The ward presented cost £3,000 and, in the hands of a less efficient and economical architect than Mr Bains, it could have cost a great deal more.

The building provided comforts for the patients and staff, and appliances and facilities for treatment which were unknown in the old ward. The new design, in which two wards were brought together at a slight angle, forming a suntrap, was not only an economy on space but was also calculated to facilitate the work of the staff to make the grouping of beds for school classes an easier proposition.

Wide windows and sliding glass screens were set in the rear walls, thus controlling ventilation, which was acceptable to the medical staff and gave more comfort to the patients. Another feature was the centralisation of the heating system. All wards received their supply from a main boiler house instead of having independent systems; this was clearly revolutionary in 1935.

As you know the hospital did more than curing, or at any rate lessening, the physical disabilities of the patients. Every effort was made to help the boys ignore any limitations, which must in some cases be there for life, and to equip them with the courage and ability to do everything as well as they could.

Party time.

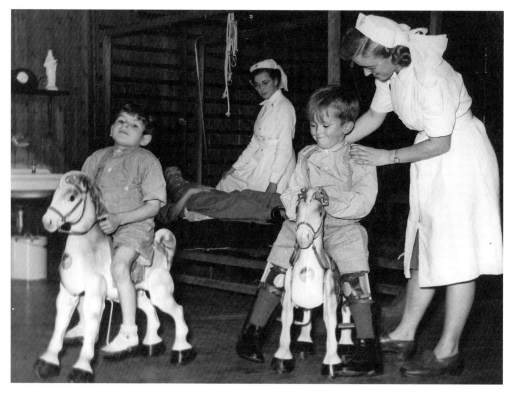

Above: Children sitting on rocking horses – good therapy for hips and good fun.

Left: Children enjoying the summer. Note the leg callipers.

Below left: School time – children playing together.

Below right: Nurses and boys on St Paul's Ward.

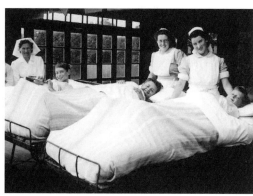

MAY 7, 1935

SCHOOL REGISTER LOG BOOK NO: 29547 MIDDLESEX EDUCATION AUTHORITY

This afternoon twenty-eight children accompanied by teacher and nurse have gone by charabanc to the Royal Tournament at the Olympia. Twenty-five more able bodied children accompanied by teacher are attending the cinema in Eastcote.

Entry written by Sr Josephine

A new children's ward called St Anne's was opened in 1937. Jack Banyard recounts his experience at St Vincent's with fond memories:

During November 1936, aged seven and a half, I was taken to Great Ormond Street Hospital, where I was diagnosed with having a polio condition which was quite severe. After nearly five weeks of treatment I was transferred, on 11 December 1936, to their country branch at Tadworth, Surrey.

A year later I was transferred to St Vincent's, where I made some progress with my mobility, but as a result of a setback I became bedridden and my early recollection was as a bedridden patient having to lay flat on a leather covered metal frame. The nurses (or Sisters) wore long, flowing, dark-coloured gowns with wide-brimmed white headgear. I was put in a brick-built ward which was fully enclosed at the lower end of the hospital.

It was very near Christmas and as the hospital was not far from my parents and relatives I had quite a contingent on one visit. I remember receiving a number of presents, but I believe there was probably a sharing policy in the hospital as some of these were taken away.

Sometimes the Chaplain showed films on the wards. The tarpaulins were drawn and we took children and adults in beds (wheels in those days) Imagine 'Mutiny on the Bounty' when the rain was blowing into the tarpaulins! We enjoyed the films, it was great fun.

Prior to St Vincent's my education had been badly interrupted. However, this got into full swing in 1938 and 1939 and, although flat on my back for a time, I received plenty of attention and help. One of the activities I remember was a sports day when bedridden patients were represented by staff members – I was lucky enough to have a staff member who won a prize for me – a toy fire engine that had headlights lit up by a battery.

With therapy and exercises the medical staff enabled me to achieve a degree of mobility and I was fitted with a full-length calliper to my left leg and a spinal brace, as scoliosis had set in.

After becoming mobile I was transferred to another ward up the hill, which was a wooden structure, open-fronted, with blinds. Soon I was required to carry out various duties, which included collecting eggs from the hen run and helping to clean out the boiler house. I believe this enabled me to achieve a degree of independence, although my parents were not too pleased when on one visit I appeared in rather a 'blackened' state from the boiler house.

For those of us who had regained mobility there was a degree of freedom and some of the boys had managed to put together a hand-controlled type of wooden 'go-cart'. As the ward 'up the hill' had a ramp, one of the lads would be pushed off, where he would trundle down the hill to the lower ward – unfortunately a member of staff appeared on the scene on one occasion and was nearly knocked off his feet – 'goodbye to the go-cart'!

Another boy had a piano accordion which we all tried to play – the song of the year was 'South of the Border down Mexico Way'.

My period at St Vincent's came to an end just prior to the outbreak of the war in 1939 when I was sent home to my parents who, I believe, were told that wards would be required because of the pending hostilities.

All in all, with the medical treatment, education and degree of freedom, I look back on my time at St Vincent's with affection and gratitude.

Judith Hawkins (*née* Walker) was a young nurse at St Vincent's but she recalls an earlier encounter with the hospital when her aunt Doris Huffer was admitted in 1936 suffering from TB spine, otherwise known as Potts Disease. Doris was a patient for many months, indeed celebrated her 21st birthday there, and had pioneering surgery which involved the removal of a piece of bone from her tibia to be made into a 'splint' for the affected vertebrae in her spine.

She spent a long time on a 'plaster bed' on St Theresa's Ward, nursed by the Sisters, one of whom was Sr Angela who later became the Matron. Doris made a full recovery and always treasured her memories of her care at St Vincent's.

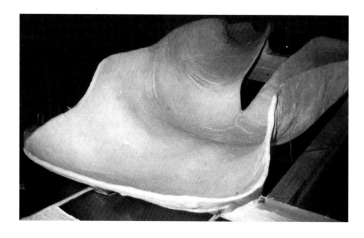

A plaster bed.

Celebrating a birthday.

The Coronation Day of King George VI did not pass unnoticed in 1937 and a good time was had by all. Thanks to the Eastcote Chamber of Commerce, a glorious tea party and a grand concert were provided for the patients of St Vincent's who were unable to go to the cinema show provided by the Council to celebrate the Coronation.

OCTOBER 3, 1938

SCHOOL REGISTER LOG BOOK NO: 29547 MIDDLESEX EDUCATION AUTHORITY

Owing to so many over 16s and such a big number being evacuated in preparation for Casualties, Class I girls has been dwindled down to the total of 6. We thought it wiser under these circumstances to put Classes I and II girls on same ward.

Entry written by Sr Josephine

The girls had the first Coronation show in the afternoon and the boys later in the evening. Special mention was made of Mr Munson, who gave a lot of time in works of this kind, and Mr A.S. Gillette, who on his own initiative to round off the feast, brought up a television set and gave the patients and staff a glimpse of this wonderful invention and hosted a variety concert.

Apart from the celebrations in the hospital, each child received a 'money' present from the Committee. The Ruislip-Northwood Urban District Council presented each child with a Coronation mug and souvenir book and arranged for about 70 of the more able-bodied children to see the Coronation film at the Ideal Cinema, Eastcote.

All the public authorities maintaining patients at the hospital on Coronation Day voted the sum of 3 shillings. per head to be expended on their entertainment.

The Queen also sent a message in which she wished every success to the fourth International Exhibition of Cripples, which was held in the Music Hall, Edinburgh, during October 1937 and was opened by the Secretary of State for Scotland.

POEMS AND RHYMES

The children were often very talented and their skills were not all practical – here are a selection of poems, rhymes and musings as part of a collection written, no doubt, during the hours in the classroom and whilst waiting for their muscles and joints to mend enough to be mobile.

OUR CRAFTY A.B.C.

Being a selection of the crafts and occupations, many of which could be written in the plural by which some of the 'Old Boys' have earned their livelihood, excluding hobbies such as bee-keeping, sketching and wireless etc.

Accountant

Bootmaker

Chauffeur, Civil servant,
    Commercial traveller

Docker, Dispenser

Engineer

Farmer, fitter

Gardener, Gamekeeper

Hairdresser

Instructor

Joiner

Kennel-man

Laundry-man

Machinist, Mechanic

Nightwatchman

Orderly

Painter, Poultry keeper

Quarryman

Reader (Press)

Ship's steward, Stoker,
    Surveyor's Clerk

Tailor, Toy-maker

Upholsterer

Valet, Variety Artist

Window cleaner

Xylographer

Yard man

Zinc worker

By Michael Quinn (1937)

A CHILD'S KISS

(Dedicated to its Mother)

With tiny arms encircled round my neck
Clasping me with fond, endearing love,
It asks a kiss, this child upon my knee,
With voice more soft and sweet than cooing dove.

And asks again, with eyes that pierce my soul,
Yet am I loath to soil such dew-kiss'd flow'rs
Which tremor in their very eagerness
Yes! Eager as a bee among the bow'rs.

Tho' worthy am I for an angels love
Since they the frailties of man must understand,
And tho' so conscious of unworthiness
Yet must I bow at this child's sweet command:

So bending down I meet those puckered lips
And feel their softness closely press'd to mine
Trembling, warm, and full of burning ardour;
Sweet-scented as the rose or fragrant 'bine.

Then sealing them to mine for one short moment,
Too brief for me e'en were it for an hour,
I realise my heart and soul are gone
Dear panting heart, for mine's within thy pow'r,

O you who'd crave a taste of heav'ns bliss,
Pray let a child bestow you with its kiss;
But do not seek therein empassion'd thrill
For such will die; a child's kiss never will.

Cornelius G. Priest (1937)

A Thin Excuse

'What makes the milk this morning seem
Like our old fashioned country cream?'
I said, with a sarcastic gleam,
To my milkman's fair daughter.
Her eyes a look of sadness wore;
'It shan't occur, sir, any more;
But since we've moved back from the shore
Our cows don't get much water.'

(1937)

A Passing Thought

Nature, impartial in her ends,
When she made man the strongest,
In justice, then, to make amends,
Made woman's tongue the longest.

(1937)

The Nightingale

The nightingale sings softly once again.
Its sweet refrain falls gently on mine ear
And, like a fire-tipp'd dart
Stabs my heart with love;
O love that's matete
For song so sweet!

With rising cadence
Fill'd with love's first joy –
Which, blind to realities of life
In nought detects alloy –
It trills its song with ever fervent zest,
Burstingly contain'd within its breast,
Yet follows soon –
Like life's fast-flowing sequence –

A sobbing note, bathed in tears of sadness,
As from a broken heart
That knows not gladness.
Still thus it sings in its solicitude,
With none to care not soothe –
Save for a cold and waning moon –
And my bard continues weeping
In a world that's sleeping.
But nay! It does not sleep
For am I not awake
And list'ning to the plaintive note? –
As one remote – yet am I one
That hears the nightingale's song

I knew not sorrow dwelt within such song
Yet am I wrong?

Cornelius G. Priest (1937)

St Vincent's

The Hospital, Oh! Awful word, a word most people dread,
They think of all those silent hours they have to spend in bed,
But if by chance they should be sent to that one on the hill,
How different their outlook, and the story they would tell.
The kindness of the nurses as they hover round the bed,
The silence of the Sisters as they float than tread,
Together with that gentle touch and then a smile to cheer,
Reminds one of the home they left and all they love so dear.
How can one dread a hospital conducted such as this?
To be in bed and see the birds is little short of bliss;
And then to see our feathered friends who always come to feed,
Gives one that peaceful feeling which in hospital we need.
The skill the doctors here display is very widely known,
And patients come for treatment here from many distant town;
So if by chance you slip and fall and break your poor old leg,
Ring up St Vincent's Hospital and ask if there's a bed.

E. Felgate (1945)

WISHFUL THOUGHTS

Oh! What torture; Oh! What pain,
They've switched the wireless on again!
Although of men there are few meeker,
I'd like to atomise that speaker.

Ain't it cold, ain't it freezin',
These 'ere beds let all the breeze in,
All my toes are froze together –
Can't we have some warmer weather!

Two and four – I ask you blokes!
I bet old Attlee never smokes.
Why can't they be one and six?
I never did politics.

R. Collins (1945)

CAROL

Once more the Christmas bells ring out
Their message of peace on earth,
And we, Thy children, kneel again
To celebrate Thy birth.
Two thousand years have passed since then,
And still man has not learned
To live in peace with fellow man;
His cities are ravaged, burned.
Teach us Thy way, Lord Jesus,
That man his wars may cease,
And the message of the Christmas bells
May herald worldwide peace.

CLB (1945)

The schoolroom fell into disuse and was used for the next ten years as a hospital shop, run by the Old Boys' Association.

The number on the school roll in 1970 varied between 110 and 125 children.

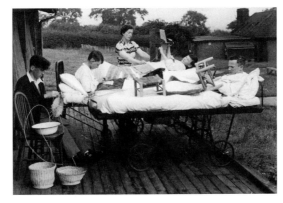

Above left: Mr Harry Errington.

Above centre: Miss Gogartey with the boys making baskets.

Above right: Practical application: cane work, *c.*1960s.

ST VINCENT'S ORTHOPAEDIC ASSOCIATION (1930)

This Association continues to give valuable assistance to the hospital.

In paying for cases for whom no public funds are available and who could not be admitted without its help. During the year the payments amounting to £317 17s 0d have been made, representing assistance to 14 cases. Grateful thanks are due to the subscribers and the county secretaries.

— ST VINCENT'S OLD BOYS' ASSOCIATION (SVOBA) —

TO PROMOTE AND MAINTAIN FELLOWSHIP AMONG 'OLD BOYS'

The Old Boys' Association was formed in 1933 and, while enjoying many social gatherings and sports days, amongst their many good works, the association tried to find employment for past patients.

The objects of the association was to 'Promote and maintain fellowship among "Old Boys"'. All patients of St Vincent's acquire an attachment to the hospital and the other patients that is deeper than will be found in most other hospitals. Even after leaving the hospital some of these friendships have continued for years, but in most cases they have faded away, for want of a connecting link. Through membership of the Old Boys Association, this link is formed, and it was hoped that the association would more strongly weld together those friendships formed at St Vincent's.

The St Vincent's Old Boys' Association started an annual reunion called the 'Rally' and they usually met on the Monday of the August Bank Holiday.

The first recorded event was in 1934, with a range of sporting events, including a four-sided 'all-in' football match; 100-yard sprint, egg-and-spoon race, blindfold wheelbarrow race, matchbox race, three-legged race, throwing the cricket ball competition, relay (married versus single), tug of war with teams picked on the field, sack sprinters and the obstacle race. Reported in *The Link* magazine for 1935 are the results for all the events.

Tea was taken in the refectory, and after much cajoling and patience by the photographer a large group photo was taken. At around 6.45pm everyone trailed down to the school where the customary concert was held, with a varied programme involving enormous hilarity and great choral renditions.

The association was also well known for the SVOBA outings, which always finished off the day with a 'dinner'.

The Executive Committee for the St Vincent's Old Boys, 1937, included:
J. Linksey (Chairman)
M. Lear (Vice Chairman)
J. Sayer (Treasurer), known as Jacko and the hospital chauffeur
G. O'Rourke (Secretary)
H. Fisher (Editor)
E. Dunne
S. Hayter

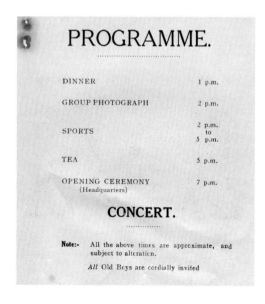

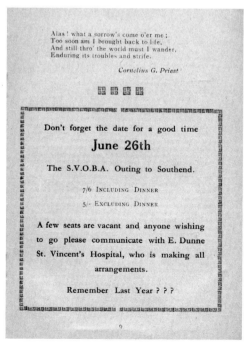

Above left: The Rally programme, 1935.

Above right: SVOBA outing to Southend.

Early Old Boys' reunion. Note the trolley.

Above left: Old Boys group photo.

Above right: Old Boys with the Daughters of Charity.

Sr Teresa Fraser DC, Matron, and Mr McCrae Aitken at the annual reunion.

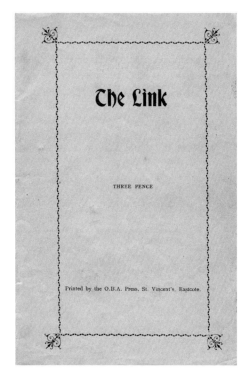

Top left: Altar servers, including a few Old Boys.

Top right: Reunion, mid–1930s.

Above left: Old Boys' reunion, early 1950s.

Above right: The Old Boys and their wives, plus Fr O'Daly, Chaplain.

Far left: The Link magazine.

Left: Association advertising its printing business.

OBJECTS OF THE ASSOCIATION

To promote and maintain fellowship among the Old Boys.
To help Old Boys by endeavouring to find employment.
To help the hospital.

The St Vincent's Old Boys' Association also aimed to provide support to those unemployed, to make connections with those Old Boys who were in work and ensure they were given suitable opportunities.

THE LINK, 1935

WANTED
An Old Boy is in urgent need of employment as a shop-assistant, checking clerk, or similar work; 12 years' reference. Please write: 68 Alderney Road London, SW1.

Above left: Mr and Mrs Jack Sayer at the wedding of an Old Boy.

Above centre: Mr and Mrs Foster; both grew up at St Vincent's.

Above right: Mr and Mrs Maher.

Left: Old Boy Guy and family at St Vincent's. Note the wheelchair.

The Old Boys' Association had a magazine, called *The Link*, and printed it on their own press in the hospital. It seems that they too fell on hard times, as witnessed by an entry in the magazine for the quarter ending 31 December 1937: 'The £25 debt remained outstanding. Having re-paid £15 as published in the last edition of *The Link*, it was found necessary to re-borrow it.'

In 1937 the Old Boys' Association annual outing was to Brighton. The start time was 8.30am and anyone who had a moveable musical instrument was asked to bring it along.

The association was running the very successful St Vincent's Press on a commercial basis, staffed by Old Boys. They undertook all kinds of printing work, including the Hospital Annual Report from 1939 to 1946.

Two ladies who were 'old patients' started the St Vincent's clothing guild to provide clothing for poor children.

Friendships and love were very much a part of St Vincent's; a wedding was a great opportunity for a gathering and there were no shortage of guests!

Rev. Fr Harrington was the resident Chaplain from 1936 until 1939. Fr Harrington moved up to London. He would be remembered for his keen interest in the choir and all things musical.

Above: Sr Vincent Neilan DC and visiting seminarians, *c.*1950.

Left: Sr Vincent Neilan DC, with the children. The teddy was given to Nurse Comdon and Nurse Kenna, donated by the Eastcote toy shop.

The wedding of David Fitzgerald and Miss Kathleen Smith took place at St Matthew's Church, Northwood, on Saturday 15 May 1937. The bride was attired in white silk and veil, surmounted by a wreath of orange blossom, and carried a bouquet of dark red carnations. The reception was held at 4 Oakdale Drive, Northwood Hills.

FIRST OLD BOYS' ANNUAL DINNER, MAY 1938

The Ship Inn in old Eastcote was the venue for the first annual dinner held on 14 May 1938, at which 30 Old Boys enjoyed soup, roast lamb, mashed potatoes and green peas, then a sweet and cheese and biscuits.

After dinner toasts to the king and the hospital and the association were proposed by W. Hagan, who very ably deputised for J. Linksey, as the Chairman unfortunately was unable to be present.

In 1938 one of the many Old Boys, Mark M. Cansick, the Honorary Secretary, wrote a plea to his many friends which indicated how difficult it could be to live within modern society and how it was important to look forward and be confident. It underlined how important the Daughters of Charity were in shaping the lives of so many:

> There seems little doubt that some of us physically disabled fellows have an inferiority complex, though exactly why seems a little difficult to explain. Seven years at the hospital convinced me that we can do most things equally as well as the able bodied man, and a number of things decidedly better.
>
> One of the most famous of all men in the world of the day was Franklin D. Roosevelt, President of the United States. He is physically disabled, the result of infantile paralysis, and he cannot walk unaided. Yet who aspires to greater heights? Many of our leading statesmen have been more disabled than the average St Vincent's boy – Philip Snowden had to use two walking sticks to get from his house to his car – but it did not prevent him becoming Chancellor of the Exchequer.
>
> In business life also, many of our great industrial leaders are physically disabled.
>
> Let us get rid of this inferiority complex, and step forward with great heart, realising that we are equal on the balance with our neighbour.

In 1922 as a seven-year-old boy, Albert Richardson was admitted to the hospital with infantile paralysis. In 1934 he was well enough to be discharged and started training at St Vincent's as an orthopaedic appliance maker. He worked in this capacity until 1974. Albert was a skilful and conscientious appliance maker.

It was noted in *The Link* in 1937 that applications for St Vincent's Hospital were on the rise; 53 patients were admitted and 54 discharged that year. Mr Batchelor of Guy's Hospital had been appointed Registrar to St Vincent's Hospital.

The Link also reported that the Fourth International Exhibition of Cripples' Work, organised by the Central Council for the Care of Cripples, would be held in Edinburgh on 13–16 October 1937 and that the winners of the Rhaiadar Jones Cup in the bootmaking class was won by the Royal Orthopaedic Hospital, Birmingham, by the pupils of Mr W. Qusen.

CARE OF CRIPPLES

Tens of thousands of disabled servicemen, returning from the battlefields of France and Flanders after the First World War could not be ignored by society and new organisations were founded dedicated to their welfare and rehabilitation.

The Central Council for the Care of Cripples was therefore set up in 1919.

At this time many disabled people spent their whole lives in hospitals and institutions, where freedom, choice and an independent life were a distant dream. In this era of the medical model of disability, the lives of disabled people were dominated by doctors and educators, and the focus of all their activities was on curing and improving the cripples to reduce the burden they imposed on society.

The Central Council's monthly publication, the *Cripples' Journal*, demonstrates how, through surgery, orthopaedics and 'improving activities' such as basket-weaving, the experts tried to do what they thought was best for their patients.

Although much of what was written at this time seems unthinkable today, there were the beginnings of an understanding that disabled people needed more control of their own lives, the removal of the barriers that prevented them from fulfilling their ambitions, and an end to the Victorian view of disabled people as nothing more than unfortunate recipients of charity and pity.

Below left: St Theresa's statue erection and blessing.

Below right: Our Lady of the Rosary statue.

BLESSING OF THE STATUE OF ST TERESA

On Friday 9 July 1937, there was great joy in St Vincent's when the Rev. Father Vernon Johnson unveiled the statue of the Little Flower.

St Vincent's fame for using every inch of available space was surpassed, and all who could fit into St Teresa's Ward were there. Among them were Mgr Jackman and Sr Visitatrice DC, who had come from Mill Hill to show loyalty to the Little Saint, with Sr Mary and Sr Teresa (Matron) joining Sisters, patients and staff.

Father Vernon Johnson spoke of the Little Flower's unbounded confidence in God, infusing even her followers to imitate her still greater devotion.

FIRE DISASTER IN 1937

The clothes, bed linen and table linen for the Sisters was all produced in a very busy sewing room as part of the efficient running of St Vincent's.

However, disaster struck on 10 August 1937 with the burning of the sewing room – a fire being a rare occurrence at the hospital, fire engines had previously only ever come to St Vincent's when inspecting the hydrants.

OCTOBER 8, 1937

SCHOOL REGISTER LOG BOOK NO: 29547 MIDDLESEX EDUCATION AUTHORITY

Owing to our fire and the burning of some of our Exhibition goods the senior girls have had to take extra time in the morning to remake the new exhibits.

I will be absent for ten days at the Exhibition in Edinburgh. Miss McKinney will take charge of Class I boys and Miss Hickey – sewing teacher will take charge of Class I girls.

Entry written by Sr Josephine

An account by 'Firefly' in *The Link* magazine gives us a flavour of what happened first hand.

The girls' workroom was rebuilt, and was being used as the hospital's sewing room, where uniforms and other items were made.

I had gone to bed fairly early, about 9.30, and I was awakened by Pat Joyce, who shares a cubicle in St Paul's Ward with me, putting on the light.

Hearing a lot of crackling, and a succession of explosions, I asked him what all the confounded noise was, at the same time thinking it was a mimic air raid that was due to take place that week.

'Sounds like a fire to me,' he said, and then I noticed he was sitting on the side of his bed trying to put his socks on, so I flung the bedclothes off me and sprang out.

Pulling aside the curtain, I saw a sight that staggered me: the girls' ward seemed to be ablaze, and well alight. I say seem, as actually it was the girls' workroom which, except for a few feet, joins on.

'Yes, it's the girls' ward,' I said to Pat, and putting on my trousers over my pyjamas, I dashed out and called the Sisters who sleep in a cubicle at the other end of St Paul's, then rushed round to call the fellows in St Joseph's, but they were getting up, having already been called. When I got over to the girls' side I found villagers and staff rushing patients out of danger, and trying to quench the fire with buckets and bowls of water.

A few minutes afterwards the first fire engine arrived, but by that time the flames were shooting sixty feet into the air and catching the trees alight nearby, and having nothing to do like, I started to make for the boys' side to get more buckets. A fireman came along and told me to get a hose. I was disappointed that the fireman did not have a helmet as I thought it was compulsory for all firemen to wear helmets.

People came to watch the fire – Wiltshire Lane, Norwich Road (the new road across Thirty Acres) and Frog Lane were choked with cars, and some of the fire engines had great difficulty getting here at all.

Being on the hill our fire could of course be seen for miles around, and a lady who lived in Pinner Green told me next day that she could hear the tiles bursting from there.

The number of beds went up again in 1939 to 209, including 24 men and 24 women.

The Matron's role required responsibility for elements of the running of the hospital included the welfare of the young patients and the activities onsite and also the conduct and attendance of all staff, including the nurses.

Matron Sr Teresa received a request from one such nurse's father – and the correspondence opposite indicates the management.

TRANSCRIPTION

Dear Sr Teresa

I hope you will excuse me writing about Marguerite's holidays.

I have to go again this year to Aix-les-bains for three weeks' cure – on the 24 of June. Last year I had to go alone, as Marguerite was already at St Vincent's and her mother preferred to stay at home to be near her.

We are a very united family and we were looking forward to go together with her and her 2 sisters. There are other considerations – for instance with a family ticket we can travel at less than half the price if she had to go later on by herself, it would be very lovely.

As you know Marguerite has been with you for just over a year and having not had a holiday, the rest and change would do her a lot of good – and I feel certain that you could rely on her gratitude, and her doing her best on her return.

My wife and I would therefore be most grateful if you could allow her to come with us on that date.

Thanking you in anticipation, believe me dear Sister Teresa.

Yours most faithfully

F. Petit

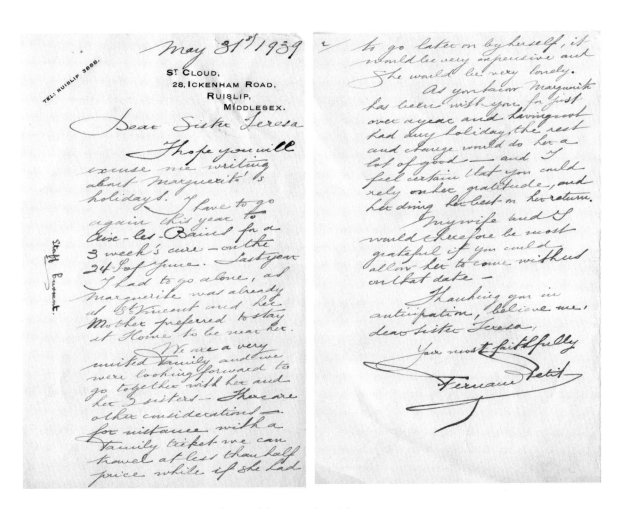

Letter from Mr Petit (father of one of the nurses) to Matron.

2nd June, 1939.

Dear Mr. Petit,

Thank you for your letter of the 31st May.
I should like nothing better than to be able to accede to
your request to allow Marguerite to have 3 weeks' off duty.
It must seem very odd to you that it would not be possible
to grant this, but I would however ask you to consider that
I have 40 holiday periods to arrange during the summer
months. To cover these, extra staff have to be engaged in
order that the services may be maintained and the holidays
have to arranged in strict series to prevent overlapping.
It is an accepted fact in every hospital that holidays can
only be granted when and as nurses fit into this schedule
and in order to meet the nurses' wishes as far as possible
I always ask them to let me know what period during the
summer they would prefer, making it quite clear that the
senior nurses must have preference and that I cannot promise
in any case that the holidays can be fitted in according
to the wishes of the staff, and especially the more junior
staff. This is very willingly accepted although it is
often impossible for me to give them anything near what

they would like. By taking your daughter out of the
accepted series of holidays, I would at once lay myself
open to demands from every junior member of the staff to
have exactly the holiday time which she wanted, which
would make the peaceful arrangements of holidays
absolutely impossible.

Marguerite will be due for a holiday period
after July and if you would wish I would be willing to
cancel her July holiday and give her a full month
during September when re-arrangement of holidays
happens to be more possible.

Yours sincerely,

MATRON.

F. Petit, Esq.,
   St. Cloud,
      28, Ickenham Road,
         RUISLIP.

Response from Matron to Mr Petit.

He chopp'd, and hack'd, and slash'd, and smote,
And mopp'd his sweating brow;
For hours with all his might he work'd
The oak refus'd to bow.
    And still for hours the fight went on,
    'til the tree began to moan;
    Then crashing, hurtling to the earth,
    It fell with angry groan.
The woodman's wrath replac'd his skill,
And care gave way to pride;
Although superior whilst alive,
Beneath the tree he died.
    The fight was o'er, the oak had won;
    It fell, yet 'twas not dead,
    But with its last and fatal blow,
    It crush'd the woodman's head.

Cornelius G. Priest.

SAVE

SILVER PAPER
USED POSTAGE STAMPS
TOOTH PASTE TUBES
DAILY MIRROR TOKENS

For St. Vincent's Orthopædic Hospital, Eastcote.

To you it is Rubbish, but to them it is VALUABLE.

THANK YOU!

Above: Fundraising – a theme running through each year (1937).

Left: Mr Snell FRCS, retiring, with Miss Bacon, Secretary of the Hospital.

St. Vincents Cripple Hospital and Home,
EASTCOTE, PINNER.

ROUTE—Harrow Road through Wembley and Harrow to Pinner. At the sign-post at entrance to Pinner turn to left for Eastcote. (The turnings will be specially marked from this point.)

:-: Programme :-:

1. Pensioners. Series of end results.

    (a) Osteoplastic reconstructions of flail elbows.

    (b) Cases of ununited fracture plus nerve lesion treated by bone graft and tendon transplant.

    (c) Fracture cervical vertebra with osteo-arthritis treated by bone graft (Albee).

    (d) Cases of repair of muscle to improve function.

    (e) Cases illustrating effect of opposition of thumb on function of fingers.

2. Children. End results in old patients of St. Vincents.

    1. Hip disease.

        (a) Recovery with some movement.

        (b) Recovery with ankylosis.

        (c) Transtrochanteric osteotomy.

        (d) Arthrodesis.

    2. Knee, old cases.

    3. Other joints.

    4. Poliomyelitis. End results after various procedures.

3. Visit wards and cases now under treatment. Workshops, etc.

4. Tea will be served.

5. Football Match. Tailors v. Bootmakers.

Programme for the British Orthopaedic Surgeons' meeting in May 1924 at St Vincent's.

Aerial views showing the extent of the grounds.

The aerial view opposite shows the extent of the hospital. The expanse of grass at the top of the picture is Haste Hill golf course, and the trees at the lower left are the start of Ruislip Woods, which contain the Lido.

John Tillyard arrived at St Vincent's during the late 1930s and he recounts his memories:

I first came to be referred to St Vincent's when my doctor, who had performed the first operation in Northwood Cottage Hospital, said he could do no more for me and that he would arrange further specialist help.

In 1939, at the age of 10, I was taken from the local cottage hospital in Northwood by ambulance to St Vincent's. I was taken in a wheelchair to the ward which to my amazement was made up of a back, two sides and a roof! The front was made of canvas blinds which were pulled down at night and they made quite a noise during the night if the wind was blowing in the wrong direction!

Within the ward were boys of my own age or older, strapped down on beds in order to try and straighten their bodies. Some of them even walked in irons – or callipers as I discovered they were called – which was a bit frightening because I had never seen anything like that.

That night I was to see someone in white coming towards me in the dark. It turned out to be one of the nuns dressed in their white uniforms and their high hats. That was pretty scary for a boy of 10 years old that still believed in ghosts! In time I got used to this scene as the nuns patrolled quite regularly.

Shortly after my arrival I met the Matron who welcomed me to the Hospital by saying they would try and make my stay as happy as possible. This was followed by a meeting with my doctor, whose name was Dr Snell, who I believe was one of only two surgeons in the hospital at that time – the other one being Dr Brockman. If only more people were aware of the marvellous work done by these two men and the fantastic operations they performed – given that the technology in those days was nothing like there is today. I must also praise the nurses and the nuns for the very efficient way in which the wards were run.

The day of my operation grew nearer and eventually I was moved to another part of the hospital where I stayed for a few days. Once the operation was over I moved back to my original ward where I found a party in full swing. It transpired that the party was for one of the boys who was going home. We were all pleased for him, although a little bit sad that we weren't going home ourselves.

When the party was over, I was taken aside by one of the nurses to have my bandages changed. At that stage I saw I had a scar from my knee down to my ankle, which was a bit of a shock, but I was soon reassured by the nurse and my doctor, who told me that he had removed two bits of bone that had turned septic as a result of the abscess bursting. Then I was told that I would be confined to bed for the next four or five months, which in the final event turned out to be eight months!

During that time I got to know a lot of the patients within the hospital, some of whom lived miles away from here and some were orphans. I was one of the lucky ones; my family came to see me every day, despite the journey from Hatch End, which in those days was quite a trek.

I saw many things during my time on the ward. One day there were two men walking around in callipers and carrying tools. When I asked the nurse what they were doing, she told me that they were ex-patients who had nowhere to go after their treatment had finished as they were orphans.

The hospital found them places to live and also trained them in different trades, such as carpenters, bricklayers, painters, metal workers, electricians and shoe makers. The shoe maker was very important to the hospital because he made most of the surgical shoes that were used at St Vincent's and other local hospitals.

They were so busy that they employed two or three men. I also learned that there was a farm where quite a few of these men worked. They had pigs and cows and grew their own vegetables, which was a great help to the hospital as the food bill must have been very high.

You didn't need to be a patient to receive excellent service from the staff of St Vincent's. My brother came to visit me one Sunday on his motor bike. The bike fell over while it was parked and the petrol tank was pierced. A young man came around the corner and saw that my brother was in trouble, and said he'd get his tools and help him to repair the damage. He was true to his word, and he enlisted the help of another member of staff who went into the town to get petrol. That's how helpful the staff were at St Vincent's.

As you can imagine, after eight months I was thrilled to be told eventually that I could go home. However, I was also very sad to leave my friends at the hospital. When I was discharged, I was advised that I attend the hospital as an outpatient for quite some time.

It was not until 1953 that I returned to St Vincent's with a lump on the side of my knee and I met up again with Dr Snell – this time my stay only lasted a few days.

The years rolled and in 1966 I had to go back again. I walked into the outpatient department and, to my amazement, Dr Snell was still there. This time my problem was diagnosed as a cyst and he told me he would have to operate to remove it. I had the operation within a matter of days and when Dr Snell came to see me after the operation I complained of slight numbness in my leg.

Dr Snell was always ready with a joke and he told me he'd chopped my leg off and replaced it with a porcelain leg, so I shouldn't experience any more problems!

St Vincent's Hospital relied on charitable help to function. The charity was the Church and public generally. Northwood people were very aware of the excellent work performed by St Vincent's Hospital and would support them at their 'open days' and charity events.

The voluntary help was excellent, including ladies visiting patients who had no visitors of their own, and also those who taught craftwork. This was extremely useful as spending a lot of time in hospital can be quite boring.

One boy was so pleased with conditions at the hospital, that he recorded his pleasure in verse during 1937.

A TRIBUTE TO ST VINCENT'S
BY BOBBY, AGED 14

There's a hospital at Pinner
A place of pure delight
Where everyone is helped along
No matter what their plight
Where invalids are cared for
And everyone is free
There's not another like it
It's a place of high degree.

The Sisters there are very kind
They do their very best
Helping you through thick and thin
With vigour and with zest.
The doctors too are skilful
They come from far and near
So you never hear a patient say
'I wish I wasn't here'.

Men's Home, 1938.

Sr Teresa Fraser (Matron) in July 1939 paid tribute to Michael Quinn who had recently died. He had been a young boy of 11 years in 1912 when he first arrived at St Vincent's.

The staff quarters and Trainees' Ward were completed and occupied by April 1939.

— Focus on Orthopaedics —

The British Orthopaedic Association (BOA)

The British Orthopaedic Association (BOA) was founded in 1918 and the surgeons from St Vincent's were part of the pioneering group, with 12 founding members. It now has over 4,000 members worldwide, the majority based in the United Kingdom and Ireland. It is a pivotal organisation within the British surgical scene, representing some 40% of the total surgical workforce.

Membership is made up of Consultants (active or retired), Surgeons In Training and Staff and Associate Specialist grades (SAS). There are over 500 overseas members.

Pioneering Orthopaedic Meeting

On 18 May 1924 St Vincent's played host to 50 eminent orthopaedic surgeons. The following letter outlines the significance of the role played by St Vincent's when Sir Robert Jones and Dame Agnes Hunt the mother of orthopaedic nursing, sat on a raised platform while they reviewed many of the young lads and their progress. The day finished with a football match in which Sir Robert 'kicked off' the first ball!

In July 1924 at a Trustee meeting Mr McCrae Aitken recommended that the Home should change its name – and so it was agreed to change the name from St Vincent's Cripples' Home to St Vincent's Orthopaedic Hospital and that a fully trained orthopaedic nurse should be in charge. This is when Sister Teresa Fraser was recommended to come to St Vincent's as Matron.

Orthopaedic Section of the Royal Society of Medicine

The Orthopaedic Section of the Royal Society of Medicine held a meeting at St Vincent's Orthopaedic Hospital on 1 July 1939, when 50 surgeons, led by Mr D. McCrae Aitken, attended and during the afternoon visited the workshops of the hospital.

St. Vincent's Cripples' Home,
Eastcote,
Pinner.

18th May 1924.

For the past week we have been making great
preparations for the big Orthopaedic meeting
of yesterday, & now we are pleased to say
everything went off very well. In the first
place we were favoured with very good
weather, the sun shone brilliantly all day,
so Eastcote looked its best. We had all the
children arranged in different groups, show-
the different stages of treatment of each
disease, such as T. B. Hips, 1st boy, acute
stage on frame, 2nd, quiescent still on frame
but ready to go into plaster, 3rd boy, in
plaster but in bed half day, 4th boy, up all
day in plaster, 5th boy walking without
plaster , cured & quite well. So/with all
                                    on
the other cases. We emptied one of the wards,
                              t
for the meeting, & had the boys on the grass
On a raised plafform in the centre, was Sir

Robert Jones, Miss Hunt, (Mother of all
Orthopoedics) her House Surgeon, & Mr Armer
of Liverpool. on chairs on either side were
about 50 other Surgeons, including some of
our local Doctors, all very interested in
the work. Facing Sir Robert Mr Aitkin
lectured on Cripples, & on the good that
could be done for them, he illustrated his
lecture with 20 cases from Shepherd Bush,
Followed by about 30 of our old boys, &
lastly of different cases in the Home.
All the old boys he found in good condition, showing no sign of relapse, & most of
them earning their own living , by the trade
they had learnt here. After the lecture
the Drs went round the different wards &
                        Robert
then had tea, Sir/was then taken down to
the Football field, to kick off for the
boys, they had a great game, the Home boys
winning, Sir Robert then left, amid the
          cheers
loud, of the boys, which we forgot to mentio
greeted him on his arrival from all the

St. Vincent's Cripples' Home,
Eastcote,
Pinner.

boys who are up, Father Hurley our old
Chaplain, was here& how he enjoyed seeing
all the old boys, his heart is still with
the cripples. Everyone was gone by about
six o'clock, we then got tea for the large
family of boys& made up beds for those who
wished to stay. So ended a very happy but
very tiring day, & we sincerely hope East -
cote will derive much benefit from it, in
days to come.

Letter following a successful BOA surgeons'
meeting at St Vincent's, May 1924.

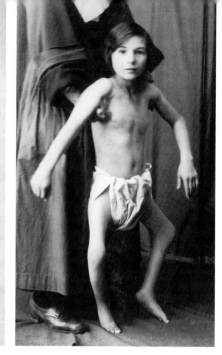

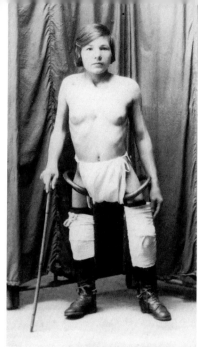

Above left: Meeting of the Orthopaedic Section of the Royal Society of Medicine, 1 July 1939.

Above centre and right: A Thomas splint used in a young girl as part of her treatment to aid mobility.

Deformity following fracture.

The history of orthopaedics goes back far beyond our own modern history and can be found in the museums displaying fossils of those in the Stone Age. There is evidence extracted from a papyrus found in the tomb of Thebes that people were suffering from TB spine, rheumatoid disease, osteoarthritis, ankylosis and kyphosis or curvature of the spine, club foot, congenital dislocation of the hip and that management of fractures was a common event in ancient Persia and Egypt, no doubt in part a consequence of building the pyramids.

The application of splints being used is evident in some tombs of ancient mummies and they are described as made of wood, bark, bamboo reeds and padded with cloth. These would have been applied by 'bone-setters', who were often local people with a high reputation for success and were frequently sought after by people who would travel from far afield to be healed. Jacquie Scott recalled:

When travelling with the British Council to Israel in the 1990s I met 'modern day' bone-setters in Bethlehem whom some families will refer to for treatment rather than conventional medicine.

With these 'bone-setters' no surgical intervention was undertaken. However, the splint would be holding a joint in what may have been a non-functional position – e.g. over the elbow with the arm outstretched. The splint was made of short, flat lengths of wood with strings of red twine wrapped around it and then padded out with some linen cloth. The splint was not allowed to be taken off and would stay on the limb for some weeks, thus allowing the broken bone to heal, but potentially limiting movement, and the end result would be a stiff non-functioning joint, not to mention the great risk of skin sores from rubbing inside an ill-fitting splint or, more seriously, nerve damage if the binding is too robust, too tight, leading to swelling and serious disablement.

Each generation has learned from previous ones and philanthropic travel ensured that new methods were shared across the continents in ancient India, China, Greece and to mediaeval Europe.

Surgical intervention and the development of an aseptic environment and shaving a patient before surgery is noted in 800 BC by Susruta, the father of Indian surgery and the equivalent of Hippocrates in his attention to detail. He believed that all patients' operating areas should be shaved, the operating room should be clean and the surgeon should have clean hands, short nails and be well-mannered.

Hippocrates was born in Cos in 460 BC and died in 370 BC and was a contemporary of Socrates. He did two things: he ran a busy, competitive private practice and he wrote a series of monographs dealing with the different diseases and issues of the body that he dealt with from a clinicians' perspective.

He established a systematic process for identifying medical science and because he was very hands-on he identified many elements of orthopaedics that modern science has developed such as dislocations – in particular shoulder, elbow, hip, knee and spinal fractures.

The Hippocratic bench or *scamnum* was one of the most important inventions in orthopaedic practice and has been used for some 2,000 years, being modified and reinvented many times. It was 'a rectangular plank, six feet long and about two feet wide' with a windlass at each end and an adjustable perineal post for counter-traction and outward leverage of the femoral head (hip). There were five or six longitudinal grooves in the lower part of the plank for the placement of wooden levers to exert pressure at either side of the hip. Other modifications were made over time.

There have been so many inventions in the field of orthopaedics that it would be impossible to mention even a fraction here, but some that link to practice and clinical developments at St Vincent's improved the lives and futures of so many and should not be underestimated.

The value of the Thomas splint – invented by Hugh Owen Thomas – (as a knee appliance) was immensely increased by the invention in 1915 in the British Army of the 'stretcher suspension bar'. The splint was in general use in casualty clearing stations and base hospitals.

The splint was primarily a padded oval metal ring covered with soft leather, to which were attached inner and outer side bars. The side bars bisected the oval ring, and were of unequal length so that the padded ring was set at 120 degrees to the inner side bar. The distal end of the two bars were joined together in the form of a W. The outer side bar was often angled out two inches below the padded ring to clear the prominence of the greater trochanter (hip).

The Thomas splint was a very popular aid to rehabilitation and used in the wards at St Vincent's and all NHS hospitals up until the early 1990s, when it fell out of favour. Modern technology and scientific progression has dispensed with bed rest, and orthopaedic patients are now up on their feet within 12 hours of surgery, with external fixators to stimulate bone and wound healing and avoid some of the many complications of bed rest.

Further developments were made in so many areas. McCrae Aitken remarked that the aetiology (cause) of scoliosis (curvature of the spine) was still very vague and that it was possibly due to a 'disturbance of reflex coordination of postural muscles'; in the 1990s it was still a challenge.

Children with tuberculosis spine being treated with plaster jackets to protect the spine from crumbling.

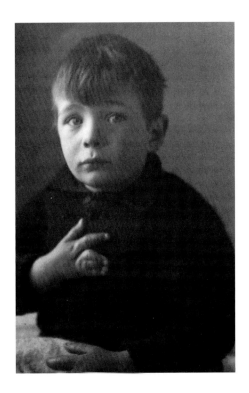
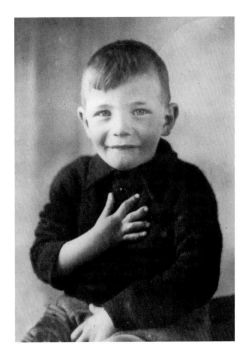

Hand deformity correction for fused fingers.

McCrae Aitken stated that in the early part of the 20th century, under Robert Jones, the treatment of plaster jackets, even when applied with suspension and lateral pressure, had been unsuccessful, so McCrae Aitken applied his plaster jackets with the patient supine in a frame, with side slings for lateral pressure and spine hyperflexed at 90 degrees. The clinical pictures show the success this brought – a considerable improvement in the treatment of severe curvatures.

It is worth pointing out that for every patient who goes through theatre there is a team of staff giving support which includes nurses, doctors, therapists, porters, cooks, schoolteachers, chaplaincy support and, of course, the Sisters of Charity.

The number of beds in 1949 declined to 176 and the weekly cost increased to £7 4s, and the Westminster Clinic closed.

The annual expenditure and average cost for each inpatient per week indicates how careful the management was to ensure funds were available to support the outstanding and challenging work.

There are detailed accounts of the outpatient activity, which was invaluable in terms of keeping people mobile and at home – something often overlooked.

The scope and range of work and demands over the decades tell both a medical and social story. It illustrates how societal changes and scientific developments have precluded us now from having to undergo such challenging disorders.

By far the most significant problems presented included tuberculosis of the spine, hip and knee, poliomyelitis, osteomyelitis, spastic paraplegia and congenital dislocation of the hip.

The 39th Annual Report (1950) provides a very interesting snapshot of the scope of work undertaken by the surgeons, nurses and Sisters at St Vincent's. The Consulting Surgeons were Mr Brockman, Mr Batchelor and Mr Snell. Sr Mary Neville was the Matron.

The following pictures illustrate some of the pioneering work undertaken by the surgeons, nurses and therapists.

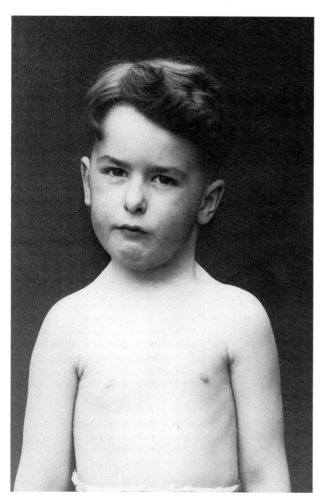

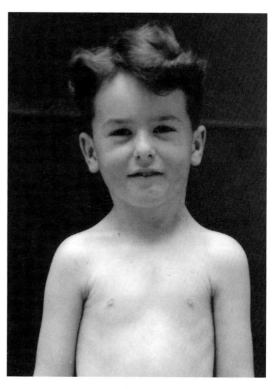

Above and left: Master Malcolm Sadler with torticolis, wry neck, and two months later.

Below: Master Hodson with spastic paralysis: dependence to independence.

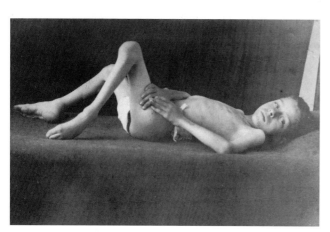

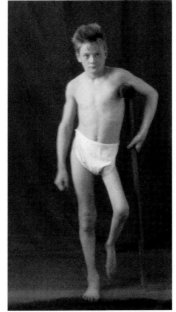

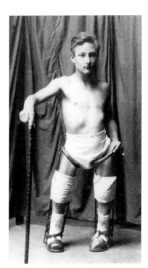

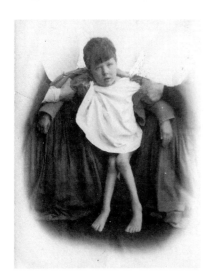

Top left: Club foot.

Top centre and right, above: Spastic paralysis.

Left: Little girl initially unable to stand.

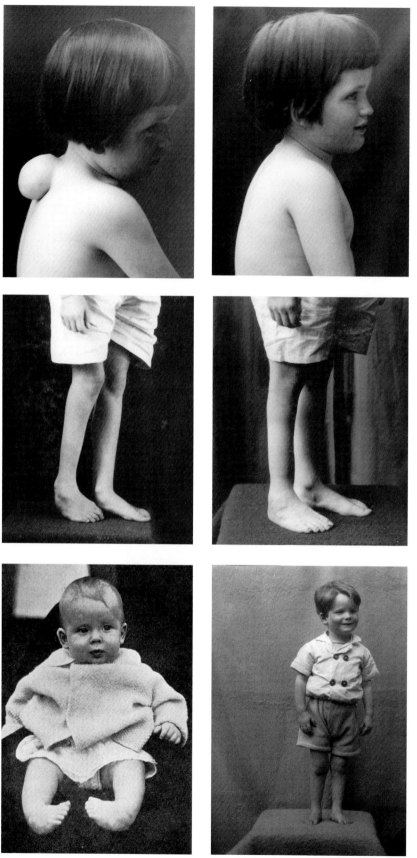

Removal of lump.

Congenital talipes equine varus (CTEV), club foot.

Club feet as a baby and then as a toddler following intervention.

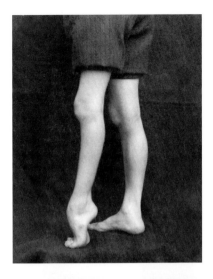
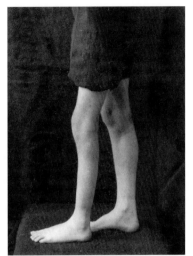

Club foot and then following surgery and splinting.

A baby with a foot deformity and then following surgery and splinting.

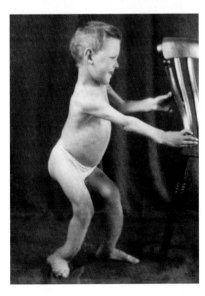
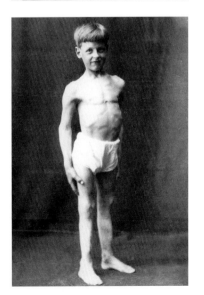

Rachitic bowing of legs transformed following specialist intervention.

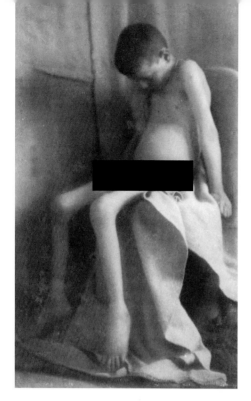

Spastic paralysis, before and after treatment.

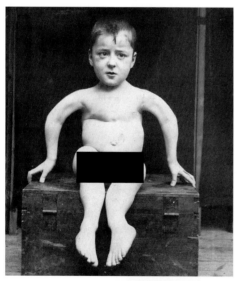

Rickets, before and after treatment.

Three friends together: Pat Simpson (*osteogenesis imperfecta*), Katy Blakellen (spastic paraplegia) and Maggie O'Donnell (TB hip).

– SECOND WORLD WAR, 1939–1945 –

The uneasy peace which had existed since the Munich Crisis was broken by the German invasion of Poland and the subsequent declaration of war by Great Britain on 3 September 1939.

Many of the orthopaedic surgeons who had been involved in the Great War were still in practice during the Second World War and so the vast experience was well utilised and there was a rapid expansion of knowledge and new techniques were employed. The main features of first aid were speed, splintage, warmth, fluids and pain relief. The types of injuries noted varied between the different armed forces. In the Royal Air Force where parachuting injuries sustained included ankle, knee and shoulder injuries, mainly on landing. Pilots could sustain fractures of the talus (ankle) due to great force on landing. Spinal fractures in air force personnel could be limited by reducing flexion and if injured during the war the fractures were reduced by hyperextension and held in plaster jackets, and early and energetic rehabilitation sometimes led to men returning to flying duties wearing a plaster jacket.

Within the Royal Navy injuries of the ankle were often sustained when individuals were knocked into the air from the deck when hit by a torpedo and in the Army when injured by landmines. Tibia fractures were very common in despatch riders.

Amputations were done far less often than in the First World War and usually only if there was gas gangrene, which had been relatively rare before 1914. The introduction of antibiotics and the reduction in tetanus saved many lives. Yet the development of blood transfusions was slow to mark change. The British initially used the direct arm-to-arm method, while the Americans and Canadians in 1916–1917 used the indirect method with preserved blood.

It was an historic day when in 1944, shortly after D-Day, two casualties were flown direct from France for penicillin treatment at St Vincent's. Penicillin could only be taken from St Mary's Ward for service cases in those days.

After the war, when penicillin was released, there was a dramatic cure of David Murray's osteomyelitis – he was one of four different cases selected for penicillin at St Vincent's and used for the first time in connection with surgery.

All these developments would later be transferred to 'civvie' street, therefore ensuring further enhancement within the orthopaedic hospitals like St Vincent's Orthopaedic Hospital and the Robert Jones and Agnes Hunt Orthopaedic Hospital – which were the first two to start – and the Royal National Orthopaedic, Stanmore and Girdlestone Hospital, now known as Nuffield Orthopaedic Hospital, all within the National Health Service.

St Vincent's and the War

With the start of the war the hospital was designated a Class 1A Casualty Hospital under the Emergency Hospital Scheme, and adults were admitted for the first time as air-raid and service casualties.

By now the hospital had 219 beds, 75 of which were designated for the Emergency Medical Service. As in most hospitals during the war there was a severe shortage of medical and nursing staff.

The work of the hospital continued normally after the outbreak of War and although there was some dislocation of hospital services during the first week in September 1939, the outpatient, massage and aftercare clinics continued their regular work. The attendances at these clinics included:

Outpatient – St Vincent's Clinic	1081
Ruislip Clinic and Massage	8944
Massage treatments – St Vincent's Clinic	9412

A total of 223 operations were performed during the year.

Classification of patients treated in 1950.

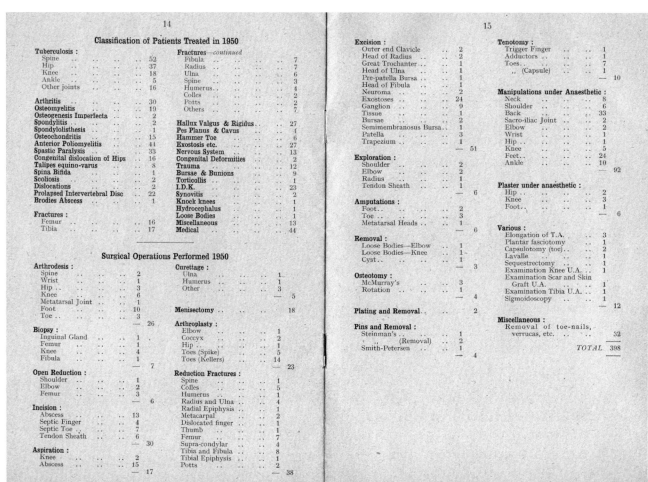

Surgical workshops attached to the hospital and mainly staffed by ex-patients were fully occupied with making surgical splints and appliances and surgical boots. These appliances and boots were also supplied to casualty hospitals in the sector under the Emergency Hospital Scheme.

Bed complement at the time:

Babies up to 3 years	24
Children 3–13 years	122
Adult – male	24
Adult – female	24
Casualty Beds	105

Ambulances transported patients to St Vincent's for orthopaedic surgery.

SEPTEMBER 20, 1940

SCHOOL REGISTER LOG BOOK NO: 29547 MIDDLESEX EDUCATION AUTHORITY

With increased air-raids and the up children having to go to the shelters the usual time table cannot be followed out. Quiet games, reading and singing have proved most successful during the raids.

Entry written by Sr Josephine

Northolt Aerodrome played a key part in the Battle of Britain and in later offensives. One third of the buildings in the area were damaged to varying degrees as a result of enemy air raids.

Within the local area 27 people were killed and 231 were injured in 57 enemy air raids when high-explosive bombs and incendiary devices, four parachute mines and five flying bombs were extracted.

APRIL 4 – MAY 22, 1941

SCHOOL REGISTER LOG BOOK NO: 29547 MIDDLESEX EDUCATION AUTHORITY

There are no entries in the school register during this period after the Chapel was hit by the bomb.

On the night of 9 May 1941, a crippled enemy aircraft jettisoned its load of three 500lb bombs on Haste Hill, which was straddled by the hospital.

Above left: Chapel.

Above right: Interior of the Chapel.

Far left: Sr Mary Neville, Matron, and Sr Francis Bailey, radiographer, examine the damage to the Chapel.

Left: The bomb damage was significant.

Below left: The aftermath.

Below right: The front entrance prior to the rebuilding of the Chapel.

The Chapel was demolished and a large piece of masonry fell through the roof of a hutted ward on the only unoccupied bed, which provided one of the most fortuitous escapes at a time when the hospital was otherwise full.

The local people thought that all the children were buried with the blasts but as they struggled up the lane they could see the children waving at them and all cheering! Despite the loss of the Chapel, miraculously there were no casualties. The Chapel was rebuilt in 1962.

With the Chapel went the Sisters' refectory and the famous glasshouse, whose metal frame was twisted beyond repair by the force of the bomb. Severe damage was also caused to the administrative buildings.

The boys' refectory had previously been converted into administrative offices, and a new dining room built at the rear of the main house.

The War Ministry hurriedly built a relief road to the hospital to retain access should the main road receive another bomb. While the mess was being cleared up a temporary Chapel was erected on the site of St Roch's Ward. It remained as the

Left: Fr O'Daly in the recreation hall 'temporary chapel'; Muriel Russell receiving Holy Communion.

Below left: Rev. P. O'Daly and Bishop Craven, a member of the Board of Management of St Vincent's.

Below right: The stained-glass crucifix in the original Chapel.

Chapel until a new one could be built and then it served as the recreation hall.

Fr Patrick Brendan Denis O'Daly was Chaplain at St Vincent's from 1945 until 1957. He was born at Brentford in 1914 and studied at Old Hall and the English College, Lisbon, being ordained at St Edmund's in 1938. His first curacy was at Kentish Town.

As you can see from the picture of the original Chapel on p.147, there were two stained-glass windows depicting St Catherine and St Vincent. St Vincent has two babies – we are told the craftsman had made a fault and filled the vacant space with a baby's head – so St Vincent is unique with twins.

LIFE GOES ON

Rationing started on 8 January 1940, four months after the outbreak of war, and did not end completely until 1954.

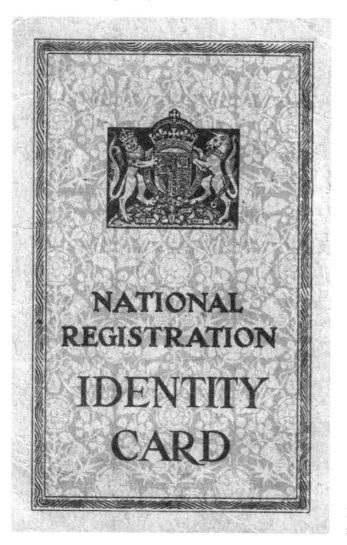

National Registration identity card.

Everybody had to get an identity card. To do this the women collected together the whole family's birth certificates and took them to their local church hall, school or somewhere designated, rather like the usage of buildings as polling stations today.

A ration book contained coupons of small squares, one for each week. These were for what the Ministry of Food considered to be our basic needs, which were tea, cheese, butter, margarine, bacon, porridge, wheat flakes and shredded wheat, lard, sugar and eggs – and no meat.

The work of the hospital proceeded, but fewer patients were treated during the war years, with the exception of the outpatients' department. This was due to the Ministry of Health placing restrictions upon admissions after D-Day and during the flying-bomb attacks on southern England. This led to a drop in admissions from 602 to 480. War workers were able to obtain treatment close to their employment, and so save valuable time at the many outpatient clinics.

A general shortage of medical staff throughout the country, combined with a shortage of nursing staff, made the work challenging at times. There were visiting staff of the hospital who supplemented the hospital team from the sector under the Emergency Medical Service. There was during this time a significant rise in the number of emergency fracture cases.

Each person was entitled to a certain number of clothing coupons which could be used in any clothing shop, and each item of clothing carried a price with the number of points needed. Coupons could be saved up over the weeks.

During the first two years of the war America did not take part as it was neutral. Canada sent vital supplies from day one and at great risk to its merchant seamen.

Messrs G. Priest, P. Joyce, and A.R.C. Renner had been made Air Raid Wardens. St Vincent's had two air-raid shelters large enough to accommodate the entire hospital, one on each side of the site, to ensure that all patients and staff could be safe and secure.

AIR-RAID PRECAUTIONS

Air-raid shelters for the patients were approved in 1940 by the Ministry of Health and completed in 1940 at a total cost of £1,398, of which the hospital was required to contribute £200 at the rate of £1 per head.

A shelter for the treatment of stretcher casualties contaminated by gas was also built – a brick building originally used as a coal shed – which cost a further £300. The resident male staff of the hospital and voluntary helpers in the district organised themselves into stretcher parties for the reception of casualties, a fire squad to deal with the initial outbreak of fire, and as watchers on the wards at night.

Sandbagging of the operating theatre, X-ray room and dispensary, and protection of glass windows from blast were inspected by the Ministry of Health, and

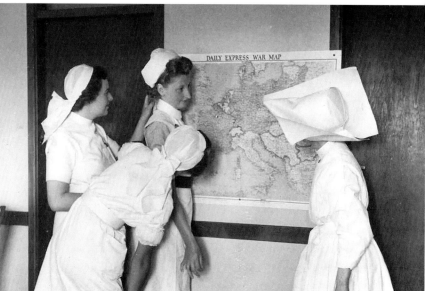

Above left: Air-raid shelter.

Above right: Sr Frances Bailey (radiographer) in front of a map, exploring the progress of the war.

adequate fire protection (fire hoses, sand, buckets and shovels, and stirrup pumps) was distributed around the hospital.

Made of concrete, the air-raid shelters at St Vincent's were certainly wide enough to wheel beds into and to house everyone. The shelter was divided into 'rooms' so that there was structure for the ceiling but also allowed some opportunity to reduce the noise and chaos that would follow an air raid.

The shelters were vast trenches cut into the ground and then covered over, leaving just a slight bump on the surface. The shelter was entered by going down a ramp and through a thick metal door. There were makeshift bunk beds and ventilation was by tubes like periscopes sticking above the surface.

The shelters had a bucket fitted with a seat for a WC, usually in a corner with modesty protected by a cloth curtain. 'My experience was that during an air raid we sat there in fear of the bombs coming screaming down and the last thing we thought of was going to the toilet.'

During an air raid, when the doors were shut, the air inside these shelters became very smelly. A combination of body odour, the toilets and the rank condensation all added to the fear of dying, which stays with you forever.

The two shelters at St Vincents were not bombproof but did offer a secure environment for the children from bomb blasts and shrapnel. When the stray bomb hit St Vincent's there was no warning and so the shelter was not in fact used.

CIVIL NURSING RESERVE

A total of 167 members of the Civil Nursing Reserve attended the hospital for training as nursing auxiliaries, and the Middlesex County Council allocated the hospital a number of trained nurses and nursing auxiliaries who could be called up for duty in emergency. (Emergency Contingency Planning, we now call this.)

Jim Laffey, a young lad at the time, recalls from his first-hand experience:

During the war we had our moments of drama with one particular night of absolute terror. Being high up we could see the reflections of the flames of London on the distant skyline.

We were near enough to Northolt aerodrome to hear the sickening thud of bombs in that neck of the woods and of course we were right under the flight path which the Germans took for their assaults on the Midlands.

That night of terror in May 1941 a crippled 'Jerry' bomber jettisoned three bombs on St Vincent's, one of which completely demolished the Chapel. God was on our side that night, for not ten feet away was a building full of sleeping domestic staff but not one suffered even a scratch.

We had our fair share of service casualties too, including three Belgian soldiers, and the hospital was a fully fledged ARP post. Many a time I manned the ARP switchboard all night then went to work the next day. Ah! To be that young again.

With the offices devastated, an old swivel ward, which could be rotated to follow the sun, previously used for isolation, was hastily converted to accommodate the Hospital Secretary and others. It still served a good purpose as the nerve centre of the Annual Garden Fetes in later years.

After the war the building of new wards continued and in time all the wooden huts were replaced by brick-built ones with south-facing verandas.

The need for intensive food production engendered an enthusiasm for allotment cultivation and the few permanent allotments were greatly added to by temporary plots, developed on parts of the recreation grounds and on private land requisitioned for the purpose. The farm production of vegetables kept the staff and patients fed.

The Middlesex War Agricultural Committee ensured that land capable of cultivation was fully used. Ruislip Common, areas of open spaces at Haydon Hall, Field End Road (site of the primary school), Pinner site (now King's College fields) and the golf courses were ploughed and cultivated.

Rev. A. Stewart was Chaplain from 1940 until 1942.

You might like to compare the 1943 rate of income tax with that of today – 10 shillings, ie 50 pence in the pound.

Above left: Front entrance to the 'Swivel' Ward.

Above right: St Vincent's gardens during the war.

The Board of Management approved the appointment of Sister Neville DC as Sister Superior and Matron in April 1942. His Eminence Arthur Cardinal Hinsley, Archbishop of Westminster, was a Trustee of the Board, along with the Hon. Mrs Henry Hope and Sir James Calder, CBE (Chairman).

The Board of Management that year included Rev. Mgr Valentine Elwes and Rev. Canon George L. Craven, who replaced Sir Cecil Pereira who had died. Sir Cecil had been a Board Member since 1909. The Resident Chaplain was Rev. Father C. Boddy. The bankers were Barclays Bank Ltd., Northwood, and they remain St Vincent's bankers in 2014.

Mr D. McCrae Aitken FRCS and Mr E.P. Brockman FRCS were the consultant orthopaedic surgeons of the day and were supported by Mr J. Batchelor FRCS and Mr V.C. Snell FRCS.

Mr Ernest Brockman FRCS (1894–1977) was what some called a sensible orthopaedic surgeon and was well known for his work with children in managing club foot. To him can be attributed developments in wrist arthrodesis. He worked at St Vincent's Orthopaedic Hospital as a visiting surgeon and was a St Thomas' Hospital graduate and an assistant to the great Mr Rowley Bristow FRCS.

At the time, the hospital boasted a holistic medical and surgical team and they included specialist surgeons Mr W.H. Ogilvie FRCS, general surgeon; neurologist Dr J. Purdon Martin FRCP, ENT surgeon; Mr A.M. Zamora FRCS, ophthalmic surgeon Mr C. Goulden FRCS, Dr J.G. Fernie LDS RCS and anaesthetists Dr J.H.G. Thompson (on active service) and Dr S.D. Adam.

The visiting surgical staff had – with the exceptions of the senior surgeon, Mr D. McCrae Aitken, FRCS and one of the registrars who had been posted to Harefield Casualty Hospital in this sector – been transferred to casualty hospitals in other sectors, but visits had been made to the hospital by specialists attached to the Harefield Hospital, and all the original members of the surgical staff still attended at the hospital.

The Board reported that the work at the hospital had gone on uninterrupted by enemy action. The total complement of beds was 219 and 15 were added by the Ministry of Health: the number of beds agreed to be provided in the case of an emergency was 75.

At the time there were 25 babies up to the age of five years, 76 children up to the age of 16, 58 men and 35 women. The first occupational therapist was appointed for bed-therapy this year. 42 acres of land, which went up to 60 acres in 1944, were cultivated for the benefit of the hospital.

Life at St Vincent's for the boys was the same as in many homes in the locality – the First Holy Communion was a very special day and was a real 'family' event.

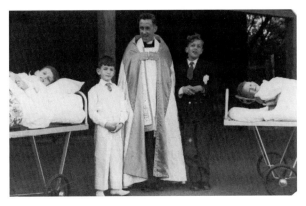

Left: Fr Galvin and boys on their First Holy Communion day.

Below left: 1942 Annual Report and statement of accounts – a designated Class 1A Casualty Hospital.

Below right: 1942 Board of Trustees, including Cardinal Hinsley.

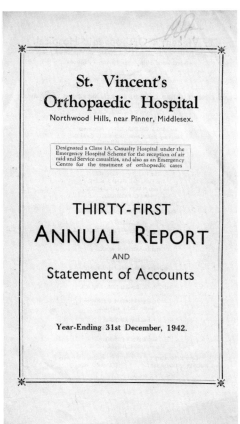

St. Vincent's Orthopaedic Hospital

Northwood Hills, near Pinner, Middlesex.

Designated a Class 1A. Casualty Hospital under the Emergency Hospital Scheme for the reception of air raid and Service casualties, and also as an Emergency Centre for the treatment of orthopaedic cases

THIRTY-FIRST

ANNUAL REPORT

AND

Statement of Accounts

Year-Ending 31st December, 1942.

Audrey Fitzherbert, General
Secretary.

Gerry Smith's story also provides an insight into the fun the children had while
growing up at St Vincent's. He went on to become a significant and well-respected
employee of St Vincent's and retired just before the site was temporarily closed in
2000. Gerry and his wife enjoyed retirement in Devon until his death in 2013.

When I was four years old in July 1942 I found myself in St Vincent's, suffering
from TB spine, elbow and hip. I lay on my back for four years in Holy Child
Ward and the treatment was 'fresh air', rest and good food.

The ward with 20 beds was a wooden building with three sides and a
tarpaulin curtain.

We were kept warm with a stone hot water bottle and in the winter, the
snow would be up to the bottom of the beds.

Every child had a hot water bottle filled morning and night to help keep
them warm, which was heavy, careful work! Before making the beds nurses had
to sweep the snow out as the children did not like the tarpaulin. We all wore
gloves and balaclavas! One surgeon inquired why the children never had colds?

One day our beds were pushed out onto the veranda and we watched a dog
fight between a German plane and a Spitfire.

Once I was up and about, when the nurses were not watching we went into
the woods to play hide and seek and of course we got into trouble when a

doctor came to see his patients and found that we had gone. We often slipped off down towards the water which is now known as Ruislip Lido and a popular place for picnics.

Mr Batchelor of Guy's Hospital was appointed Registrar to St Vincent's Hospital in 1937 and visited regularly.

Sr Mary Jo Powell arrived after the war as the radiographer but later was asked to take over as Sister in charge of a ward to cover illness. She recalls that a visiting consultant surgeon, Mr Batchelor FRCS from Guy's Hospital, arrived unannounced on the ward to do a round and was not pleased to find that nearly all the boys had disappeared into the woods to play.

He said that 'he had not come to the hospital to look at the scenery!' Needless to say, Sr Mary Jo sent a nurse out to find the boys – many of whom were quite able to get about with splints.

Mr William Hagan, as a young lad, learned his craft at St Vincent's and went on to share his great skill and talent, running the tailoring workshop teaching the many young lads for many years. He goes on to recall:

It was shortly after England had declared war on Germany that my acquaintance with St Vincent's Hospital began. What a contrast! London, with all its bustle and confusion; Eastcote with its green fields, and winding lanes. The country, as Eastcote was then, looked delightful, the song of birds, the scent of hay, and the cattle in the fields, made a great change from the 'honk honk' of motors, the smell of petrol, and the traffic.

Eastcote Station, 1938.

Well do I remember the ride from Eastcote Halt in Mr Wright's cab. I began to wonder whether Eastcote had any inhabitants at all, until I reached the Iron Bridge, where there was some sign of life. However, like all things, the journey came to an end, and we arrived at the glasshouse, to be met by the Sister Superior. After answering the usual questions concerning the journey, I took leave of my guardian, and was sent to St Vincent's shed, where I was handed over to the maternal care of Mrs Murphy, who did all she could to get me accustomed to my new life which, I found later, was to be entirely different to the one I had been leading. The first thing I discovered, was the necessity of learning a new language, with such words as 'snags', 'crodge', 'dork', and many others, too numerous to mention, which left me completely in the dark as to their meaning. My shed mates in those days, to mention a few were: Frances Newman (Polly), Henry Davis (Butcher), Tubby Harrison (Blackberry Pie), David Riley and George Field.

I was introduced to the late Mr Glynn, which went something like this; 'Sir, here is a new tailor to be.' 'What regiment does he belong to?' asked Mr Glynn. Seeing that I did not understand, somebody told him that I was minus a leg, so I was nicknamed Jack Lahemmy, but, who that person is, or what his qualities are, I do not know. However, I soon found Mr Glynn to belong to that school of teachers who have a way with them in the art of teaching, and wonderful ways of expressing their thought; there is no doubt he was a past master. He had a great deal to do with us, as it was his duty to see us safely in bed, which recalls the occasion when Mr Glynn, who was very fond of rambling in the woods, lost himself. It was quite a good thing for the chaps who were late, but not so good for him, as he had visions of being in the wood all night, instead of a comfortable bed.

In conclusion, I would like to pay a tribute on behalf of all the 'Old Boys' of those days, to Father Hurley and to thank him for his many kindnesses.

Boys always enjoyed fete day, helping on stalls and meeting people and sneaking into the beer tent trying to sample the drinks. We were not allowed to mix with the 'girl patients' unless there was a concert, when we were all taken to the hall although the nuns didn't approve of the amount of leg shown by some of the ladies who were visiting!

Gerry went on to stay at St Vincent's as an employee and left when the hospital closed in 1999.

Christmas parties in 1944 were held by the United States troops and another by the Anti-Aircraft Units. The entertainments made that Christmas an outstanding occasion for many of the little patients.

Gerry Smith recalls that visitors came at weekends bringing presents and sweets and 'being an orphan I was upset sometimes as I had no visitors but I did manage to scrounge some sweets off the others.'

Left: Advertising Board for 'third' Garden Fete, 1944.

Below: Garden Fete, 1944.

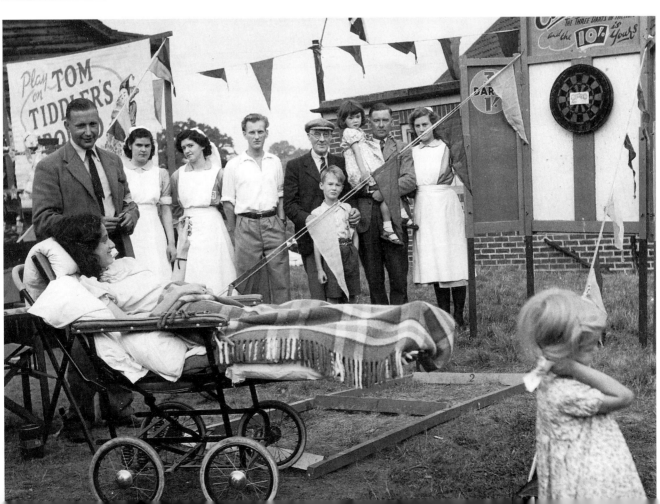

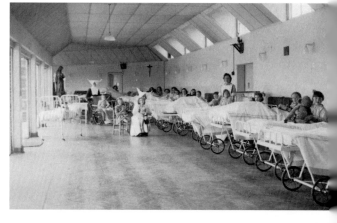

Above left: Magician David Ball entertaining
the boys.

Above right: Sr Joseph Powell DC and the
new St Margaret's Ward.

Right: Babies' ward (Holy Child Ward).

Below right: Small children playing.

Bottom right: St Margaret's Ward: girls
playing with the doll's house.

Below: Sr Magdalen and baby.

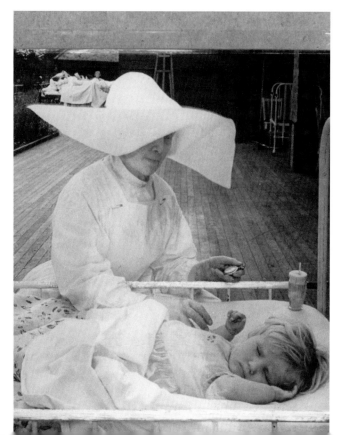

The nuns slept in wooden sheds around the grounds, but in 1965 they had their own house built close to the new Chapel.

The staff doctors came from London hospitals of Guy's and St Mary's and the local hospital, Mount Vernon. The house men lived in the flat attached to the Chaplain's house on site and the nursing staff lived in the nurses' home – it was truly international – and the 'Home Sister' served meals.

Mr Vincent Snell, orthopaedic surgeon used to regularly ask if it was 'jelly day', meaning was it a 'feast day' – in which case he would stay for the meal as it was extra special.

Other lay staff lived out locally. Sr Angela was the tutor during this time and also an examiner for orthopaedics along with Sr Margaret Woods. Sr Clare O'Driscoll became Sister tutor later.

Gerry Smith remembers a Tate and Lyle package: 'Matron (Sr Vincent Neilan) opened it – full of money – notes everywhere! This happened two years running; we always thought "conscience money" but no clue as to who was the sender.'

On the wards there were many parties, with local people visiting and of course Father Christmas. During Christmas students used to help with the Royal Mail. Vans came and mail was sorted in Matron's office.

Above and right: Boys playing.

Bottom right: Fun with the pet rabbits.

Below: Nurse Kenna with the boys on St Paul's Ward by the crib.

Gerry recalls: 'During the 1940s Mr Harry Neal provided much welcome fire-wood for the hospital. I remember the postman bringing a doll for one of the girls on St Margaret's Ward.'

CHRISTMAS TIME ON ST MARGARET'S, 1945

Christmas is a very jolly time on St Margaret's. Kind people from outside remember us each year, by sending us lots of toys and presents for Christmas.

The ward is decorated beforehand by the teacher, who very kindly offers to do it. When the decorating is completed, the ward has a very festive appearance. A big Christmas tree is placed in the middle of the ward, and decorated by the nurse with fairy lights and other decorations. Then a beautiful crib is erected near Our Lady's altar.

Round about Christmas Eve the carol singers come and stand in the middle of the ward, and cheer us by singing the well-known carols.

On the night of Christmas Eve each of us hangs up a large bed-sock and during the night the Staff Nurse, or one of the other nurses, fills them with presents. The little girls on the ward believe Father Christmas has really visited them.

Christmas carollers.

Almost at daybreak on Christmas morning everybody is awake and there is great bustle and excitement on the ward. We all open our stockings and look at our presents, and instead of the place looking like a ward, it looks like an untidy paper-shop! (Most of us, when we unwrap our parcels, throw the paper on the floor!)

Here in the hospital, we do not forget that Christmas Day is Our Lord's birthday. When we are ready, we are taken into the dressing room, so that we can compose ourselves and prepare for receiving the greatest Christmas gift – Our Blessed Lord Himself. The priest comes round, and the greatest moment of the day is now here- Our Blessed Lord comes down into our hearts. We stay making our thanksgiving, until the nurse wheels us back to the ward again.

After a good breakfast, we play with our games, and sing carols until dinner time. Then we have a good dinner of turkey and roast potatoes and other good things. Eventually the Christmas pudding is brought out. When that is finished, nuts and raisins are shared out amongst us. During the afternoon we have a marvellous party, to which everyone looks forward eagerly. The Sisters and many other people are invited to it. There is a gorgeous big Christmas cake in the middle of the table, and lots of other sweet things to eat.

After we have finished eating all we want, one of the nurses tells us they have a big surprise for us. We all wait patiently to see what is going to happen. The door opens and out walks Father Christmas with a big sack of toys on his back. Everybody cheers him loudly. He walks to the Christmas tree, and opens his sack, and gives each of us a present from it.

A moment that everybody has been waiting for comes at last. Father Christmas walks up to the Christmas tree, and stands on a chair to strip it of its lovely presents. Each of us waits to see what we are going to get from the tree. It is then stripped of its lovely presents, and all that remains are the fairy lights and other decorations. We all thank Father Christmas for coming to the party, and giving us the lovely presents. Then he walks off the ward.

Everything is cleared up, because it is getting rather late. We all try and tidy our beds, ready for the Sisters and nurses to sing carols. When we are ready, the carol singers stand in front of the crib and sing many of the carols we know. Prayers are said rather late on Christmas night. Then we settle ourselves down comfortably, after a very exciting and enjoyable day.

Gerda Schonbrunn and Marion McKernan (girls on St Margaret's)

Christmas was like everywhere else. The children were excited and it was difficult to get them to go to sleep. Every child had a stocking at the end of their bed. After breakfast on Christmas Day we would open presents from Father Christmas. Every child had plenty of gifts from parents or from the Sisters. Visiting was an open event all day, and after dinner with parents staying, we would then as part of the tradition have tea served by the nurses using the 'best china'.

The following is an example of a letter sent to Father Christmas to ensure he did not miss St Margaret's Ward one year.

Dear Santa Claus,

We are sending you this letter from a hospital called St Vincent's. One little girl says you know where it is because you have been here before. When you come to visit us this year will you please come to St Margaret's Ward first? All our bed-socks and pillow cases are ready to be filled. These are some of the things we want: Dolls, dollies' beds and prams, tea-sets, puzzles, reading and drawing books and handbags with purses, mirrors and combs in them. On Christmas Eve we will go to sleep early and hoe the next morning will soon come. Please bring all the presents together this year. Somebody told us that one Christmas Eve you came here twice because you did not bring enough presents the first time. There are about fifteen little girls on the ward now, but we may have a few more at Christmas, so don't forget to bring some extra presents. We hope you remember where our chimney is. It is in the kitchen roof at the back of the ward. You will have a tight squeeze getting down – be very careful you don't get stuck.

With lots of love and best wishes
From St Margaret's Little Girls (1945)

Nurses would be wearing their navy cloaks turned around to show the red lining and join the men to go about all the wards singing carols. It was a magical and very happy time. All the wards had their own special crib too.

Christmas was a wonderful time at St Vincent's for all boys and girls. Sr Anne Remmen made the crib which could be folded up and put away and the figures (about 100 years old) are still used in the nursing home today. Sr Gerald Byrne organised the choir.

Gerry Smith recalls: 'after 18 months working on different jobs in England, I returned to St Vincent's and started work in the laundry, maintaining machines, firing boilers, then two years later I moved to the splint shop, making callipers and frames for spinal cases. Eventually in 1974/5 the splint shop closed and I moved to the maintenance department. I stayed there happily until 1998 the hospital closed and I was made redundant and later moved to Devon. I had some good times at St Vincent's and made very good friends who looked after me.'

His Grace the Most Reverend Bernard Griffin, Archbishop of Westminster, Trustee of St Vincent's Board visited St Vincent's on 23 June 1944. He spent several hours visiting the entire hospital and it was evident that he was keenly interested in the work and of individual patients.

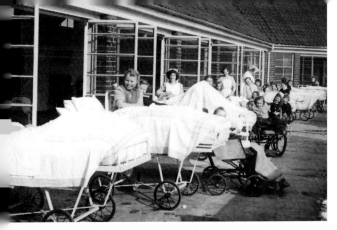

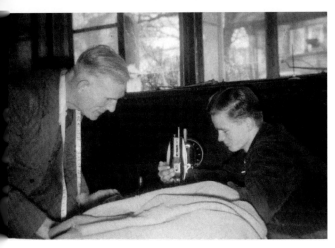

Above left: St Margaret's Ward and Sr Mary Joseph Powell DC.

Above right: Crib with original St Vincent's statues as seen in the Nursing Home.

Left: Mr Hagan and Gerry Smith in the workshop.

Below left: Christmas.

Below right: The Bed Post cover, Christmas 1945.

SANTA CLAUS

This is how the story of Father Christmas, or Santa Claus, came into being.

Years ago there lived a man named Nicholas who later became St. Nicholas. At Christmas time he thought he would like to give a present to everyone in the village. So he got some money and went to the nearest town, and bought lots of toys and presents in a large sack, and waited until he thought all the children would be in bed and asleep. He started to walk down the snow covered street. At the first house he called, the people accepted the presents joyfully. But at the second house the people were rather suspicious, because they could not understand Nicholas giving things away, and wanting nothing in return. They thought there was some trick in it, so they shut the door in his face.

But Nicholas was determined that they should have their Christmas presents, so he climbed up on to the roof and found a chimney with no smoke coming from it. He took the presents from the sack and dropped them, one by one, down the chimney.

That is how the story that Santa Claus (St. Nicholas) comes down the chimney to bring the presents for your stocking on Christmas Eve began.

ROY BUTTERWORTH.

20

In the Christmas 1945 first edition of the in-house magazine called the *The Bed Post*, produced by members of the hospital staff, was a poem about how they felt about St Vincent's.

The illustrations in *The Bed Post* magazine were from the Women of Nazareth, Field End House, Eastcote, more familiarly known as the Grail – they waived the copyright and allowed the free use of plates. Jim Laffey did the typing in preparation for the production to be made.

On Sunday afternoons we call,
At St Vincent's Hospital;
The smiling faces first we see,
And then, oh Boy! That cup of tea!
Next we have our little chat,
Talking 'bout this and that,
Till it's time once more to roam,
To that fire we left at home!

O.G. Kelly, *The Bed Post,* 1946

SOME SHORT UPDATES WITHIN THE 1945 CHRISTMAS *BED POST*

CLUB ITEMS

The Club have been quite successful so far in their table tennis matches, having won four games out of five played. We were beaten by St John's Young People's Guild.

On 13 November we played a team from Sacred Heart Church Ruislip and beat them.

The 'Shack' is now reopened as a 'quiet room'. We have to thank Sister Mary for all she has done to help. There is some comfortable furniture and an excellent heating system both help these days.

Bill Quinn

CHILDREN'S PARTIES

Various friends of the hospital have again been most kind in giving the children treats. Miss Warrender's summer party in the grounds of her house in Eastcote is always looked forward to eagerly and always comes up to expectations. Miss Anita and Miss Peggy Fielding again invited a contingent to Stoke House, Slough, for a Christmas Party. The Hon. Lucy Verney Cave took a number of children to the Zoo. The girls of Sacred Heart Convent, Roehampton, who took particular interest in St Vincent's, invited them to a party to spend the day at Roehampton which they all thoroughly enjoyed.

WIRELESS APPEAL

The final result of the Broadcast Appeal made by the Right Hon. the Viscount Fitzalan of Derwent KG was about £478, and we would like to take the opportunity of thanking both the BBC and all those who responded so generously. The appeal was made for the New Girls' ward.

ALEXANDRA ROSE DAY

The hospital became involved in the Alexandra Rose Day because it was and still is a charitable fundraising event that has been held in the United Kingdom since 1912. It was first launched on the 50th anniversary of the arrival of Queen Alexandra, the consort of King Edward VII, from Denmark. The Queen requested that the anniversary be marked by the sale of roses in London to raise funds for her favourite charities. The Queen developed an idea which would benefit the funds of London hospitals through the sale of artificial wild roses, which were to be made by people with disabilities.

The day was to be called 'Alexandra Rose Day,' and the initial drive swept Londoners off their feet. The first event raised £32,000 (the equivalent of over £3 million in 2014 money). The funds raised were a great benefit to hospitals, and the annual drive became an institution, one of the chief attractions of London's summer, with Alexandra the star. By 1920, £775,000 for London hospitals had been raised. Queen Alexandra's last Rose Day was 1923, the 60th anniversary of her arrival in England. She died two years later, in 1925.

Today the event raises money for charities that do not normally get national attention for fundraising. The Prime Minister traditionally launches the day by being the first to buy a rose.

In 1945 the sum of £50 was received from the Alexandra Rose Day Fund. The Rose Days each year are organised by volunteers and the sums realised could not have been raised without the indefatigable aid of all these volunteers who gave generously of their time to selling roses in the town centres, railway stations and offices.

With the end of the war in 1945 one men's ward reverted to boys' use. The clinic at Leatherhead closed, leaving the three: at Westminster, Ruislip and in the hospital.

The Ruislip clinic had been using the Catholic Church Hall until 1942, when it moved to larger premises at 26 Brickwall Lane, which in turn closed in 1976.

The extra 10 acres of land rented during the war for cultivation were relinquished leaving 50 acres, which provided about one-third of all the hospital's food requirements. 1945 saw the reinstatement of the Girl Guides.

The proprietor of the Orchard Hotel had for a number of years, starting in 1943, given permission for a 'bring and buy' in aid of St Vincent's. It was always a successful and happy event.

The Annual Garden Fete in 1945 was opened by Messrs Flanagan and Allen, persuaded by Charlie Kunz, who was once a patient at St Vincent's.

As music hall comedians they would often feature a mixture of comedy and music in their act, which led to a successful recording career as a duo and roles in film and television. They were also famous for songs like 'We're going to hang out the washing on the Siegfried line' and 'Underneath the arches'. They were also well known for being a part of the Crazy Gang.

The Third Generation: 1945—2005

— After the Second World War —

There was uncertainty for the hospital in 1946 with the lack of clarity on voluntary hospitals in the advent of the New Health Act, which was introduced in 1948, effectively starting the National Health Service. By far the biggest event of the early post-war years was the inception of our National Health Service – 5 July 1948 – when medicine and health care became free (funded by taxation) and folks could go into hospital without the worry of who was going to pick up the bill.

St Vincent's was in a bit of a quandary. Religious Institutions were among those that were being disclaimed by the Ministry of Health and it was to remain a voluntary hospital still under the Daughters of Charity.

The problem was funding: who would choose to be admitted to St Vincent's if they still had to pay for their treatment? The NHS Authorities and St Vincent's eventually came to an agreeable arrangement whereby the NHS would pay for running costs, but the hospital would be responsible for the capital costs. The expansion of St Vincent's therefore continued and NHS patients were referred for orthopaedic care.

The Board of Management made an appeal to the number of supporters who had withdrawn their subscriptions as people were worried the government would benefit from their donations.

St Vincent's emphasised that all monies and gifts to a particular hospital would remain the property of that hospital, all pre-existing endowments would be honoured and hospitals with religious associations would be allowed to perpetuate those associations and characteristics. The number of beds was reduced to 200 and the weekly cost per patient increased to £4 9s 6d.

St Vincent's had been in operation for 36 years by this time. The hospital remained a voluntary organisation but, by arrangement with the North-West Metropolitan Regional Hospital Board, patients in the ordinary wards were not called upon to pay anything towards their maintenance.

Part of the cost of maintenance and all capital expenditure had to be met from voluntary sources. The hospital therefore looked towards its friends to provide support to ensure the service could continue.

Michael Dickens was a young lad at the hospital in 1946–1952 and during this time he recalls some very treasured memories of the community and in particular Sr Margaret, later to be known as Sr Theodora (when Sisters reverted to their own names), and Sr Mary. 'They truly cared for me and educated me, not just to read and write but to accept God's love and to praise Him.' Sr Theodora ran the outpatients' department for many years. It is important to note that a local road in Northwood Hills just down from St Vincent's is named after her – Theodora Way.

By the age of 18 Michael was able to pass exams and he had a very successful career working as a research scientist in molecular biology for the Medical Research Council at Kings College in London University. He published numerous papers and in 1978 he was awarded a Gold Medal by the Royal Microbiology Society for his contribution to science.

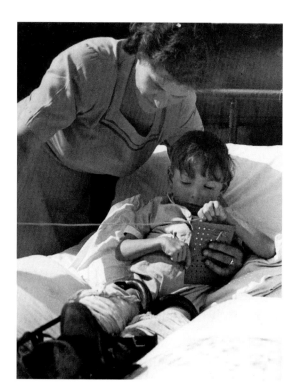

Left: Michael Dickens.

Right: Victor Anscomb, with TB hip, and his mum on St Michael's Ward (1948–57).

Once Michael retired he turned to his hobby collection of 20th-century British art and was curator of many exhibitions in London and San Francisco. Michael felt that his preparation for life's work was firmly led by the care and admiration for the community at St Vincent's and he was elected and trained in the healing ministry at his church.

The hospital magazine *The Bed Post* of October 1946 provides us with an insight into life post-war; while very much still under rationing there was no rationing of humour.

This extract cites a Medical Medley:

ABDUCTION FRAME: 'She was only a beautiful picture, in a beautiful golden frame'.
ALBEE: Chills run up and down my spine.
ANGINA PECTORIS: There's a blue ridge round my heart.
ANAESTHESIA: (local) Your tiny hand is frozen.
ANAESTHESIA: (general) Beautiful dreamer, awaken to me.
ASTHMA: This'll make you whistle.
AURICULAR FLUTTER: Why does my heart go boom?
CLAUSTROPHOBIA: Don't fence me in.
CONCUSSION: I saw stars.
CONJUNCTIVITIS: Dancing with tears in my eyes.
CONTUSION: Deep purple.
GYMNASIUM: He flies through the air with the greatest of ease.
HALLUX VALGUS: Up on your toes.
INSOMNIA: With my eyes wide open I'm dreaming.
OSTEOTOMY: He broke my hip in six places.
OPEN WARDS: When the moon shines over the cowshed.
THEATRE: A little bit off the top'll do for me.
X-RAY: I guess I should have seen right through you.

Mary Gallagher, *The Bed Post* (1946)

Here also is an extract from a letter written in 1946 by one of the children to Father Christmas:

We were all very pleased that you didn't get stuck in the chimney last year, and we hope you will manage just as well this time. Don't forget that we are leaving a piece of bread and jam and a cup of milk on the kitchen table. We hope you will enjoy it, and whatever you do, don't slip on the lino in the kitchen – it wasn't there last year. We send you our love and best wishes, from your little pals on St Margaret's Ward.

Above: Sr Angela Murray and the student nurses.

Right: Annual Report, 1948.

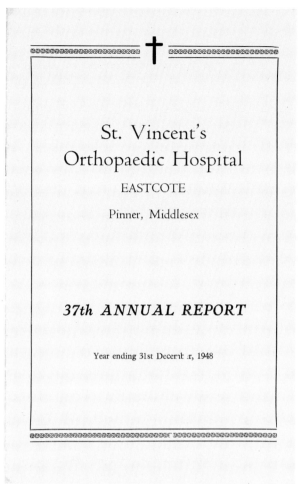

St. Vincent's
Orthopaedic Hospital

EASTCOTE

Pinner, Middlesex

37th ANNUAL REPORT

Year ending 31st Decent r, 1948

Sr Kevin Thompson took over as Headmistress for the children's school in November 1947.

In 1947 the School of Nursing was approved by the General Nursing Council for training of orthopaedic student and pupil nurses.

By 1948 11 nurses had passed the Final Orthopaedic Examination and 12 the Preliminary State examination, and a study room for the nurses was erected at a cost of £700. However, during the year nursing was carried on under great difficulties owing to the shortage of nursing staff.

The Annual Reports depict a vivid picture of the life at St Vincent's and this provides a snapshot of events in 1948.

The weekly cost per patient had now risen to £5 8s 3d.

TRIPS AND EXCURSIONS

Members of the Rotary Club took some of the boys by car to Burnham Beeches – a thoroughly enjoyable outing. A number of churches and schools in the neighbourhood sent harvest festival gifts of fruit, vegetables and flowers, which were much appreciated by the patients.

Left: Harry Errington (driver) with the three Sturgess brothers at Dymchurch on a seaside outing.

Below left: Bertram Mills Circus.

Below right: Dymchurch.

SEASIDE AND SAND

Seaside trips to Dymchurch in Kent were often helped by people from Eastcote Parish and the youth club. They would be seen filling up a furniture van with all the splints and wheelchairs.

Then a coach for the children, Sisters and staff in cars for the adult helpers all set off in convoy to the coast for the day. Quite an expedition!

The circus world of sawdust and spangled lights was laid wide open for 40 St Vincent's children when they paid a ringside visit to the Bertram Mills Circus at Olympia, made possible by Mr William Old from Harrow. For many of them it was the first time to see trumpet fanfares, aerial and animal high jinks, clamouring clowns and jocular jugglers.

Visits to the Royal Tournament and the circus at Olympia by all those children who were able to travel occurred thanks to the generosity of the organisers of those events.

Another very exciting venue was Northolt aerodrome with Christmas parties hosted by the Royal Air Force, the United States Air Force and Infantile Paralysis Fellowship. Visitors to St Vincent's included the students from St Lawrence's Church Choir, Eastcote; Strawberry Hill and the Hendon Operatic Society.

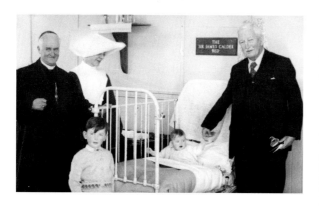

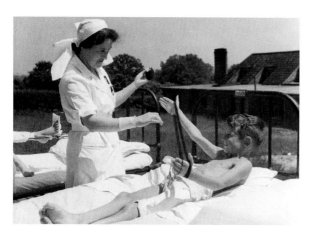

FRIENDS OF ST. VINCENT'S

A group of local residents, business and professional men under the anonymity of the title "Friends of St. Vincent's Hospital" held a fund raising dinner and dance at the Tithe Farm, South Harrow on Wednesday. It is anticipated that over £150 profit was made.

HOLD CHARITY BALL

Chairman Mr. Percy Pyett is the first arrival to have a red carnation pinned in his button hole by a St. Vincent's nurse.

The fact that this basket of fruit fetched over £20 is not so surprising when the auctioneer is recognised. He was Mr. Frank Rowe, of Ruislip, who, in famous West-end auction rooms, has auctioned over 26,000 greyhounds.

The party spirit soon took command, and here is Mrs. Warden wife of a committee man making her contribution to the cabaret.

Mr. and Mrs. Tommy Kemp, well-known band leader and his wife are presented with a spin dryer, first prize in the draw. In the centre is Weekly Post Newspapers managing director Mr. Ronald Richards, who made the presentation on behalf of the committee.

So successful was this first Friends of St. Vincent's Ball that the committee have decided to follow it up with a buffet dance at the Tithe Farm, South Harrow on February 11. Tickets, 10s. 6d. each are obtainable from the chairman, Mr. P. Pyett, 1 Shenley-avenue, Ruislip.

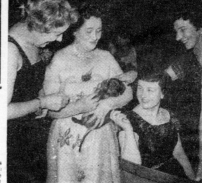

Centre of many admiring eyes was a few weeks o'd miniature Dachshund, nestling here in its owner's arms. Mrs. Pyett, owner of a string of racing greyhounds took the puppy to the dance intending to auction it in aid of the funds. But her fondness for dogs forbid her, and home it went again.

Top left: Bishop of Westminster, Rev. George Craven, Sr Vincent Neilan DC, Aiden and Sir James Calder (Chairman, 1955).

Centre left: Anthony Janssens, Sr Vincent DC, Mr Stokes and Miss Bacon at the fete, 1956.

Bottom left: St Paul's boy helping the nurse.

Above right: Friends of St Vincent's Charity Ball.

Below right: The statue Our Lady of Fatima is currently in the gardens of St Vincent's Nursing Home (2013).

After a slow start following the war and rations, the workshops within the hospital eventually became fully operational again with a great number of splints and boots being made to supply patients under the Health Act.

A number of boys were trained in both the boot shop and tailor's shop, going on to make successful careers.

Supplies from the farm ensured the health of patients was maintained, with supplies of fresh milk and eggs providing more than 50% of the total consumption, and meat, garden vegetables and fruit about one-third.

The Trustees during 1948 included His Eminence Cardinal Bernard Griffin, Archbishop of Westminster, the Hon. Mrs Henry Hope and Sir James Calder CBE.

The Board of Management comprised Sir James Calder (Chairman); Rev. George Craven (Auxiliary Bishop of Westminster); the Hon. Mrs Stirling (the sister of Sr Teresa Fraser), Miss C. Faudel-Philips, the Hon. Mrs Henry Hope, the Hon. Maud Acland-Hood, Mrs C. Passmore, Mark Gilby and Sister Superior of the Daughters of Charity.

FRIENDS OF ST VINCENT'S AND CHARITY WORK

The Friends of St Vincent's continued to fundraise and the paper clipping opposite shows they knew how to have a great time.

Many of the children were all moved into one of the largest wards and they were then entertained by the principals and cast of the pantomime 'Cinderella' who were then playing at the Coliseum and were provided with an impromptu entertainment.

One year we did a pantomime – 'Snow White and the Seven Dwarfs'. Terry Eager worked backstage doing music. Paddy Stack was a dwarf walking on his stumps.

THE GROTTO, 1949

The grotto was made by the hospital male staff and the statue purchased with subscriptions given by the hospital staff. In October 1949 the new statue was carried in a torchlight procession from the Chapel, blessed and installed in the grotto.

Sr Carmel recalls when the statue disappeared from its home near the mortuary in 1995 on the feast of Christ the King (last Sunday of the Church year, before Advent).

During that time Gerry Smith used to walk his two dogs up through the woods and down to his own house in Fore Street regularly, he was always on the lookout for the statute, just in case it had been left in the woods, but to no avail, and this went on for months.

Then one Sunday morning in summer Sr Carmel, who was Matron at the time, recalls Alan Edmundson, General Manager, suggesting that it was perhaps time the statue was replaced as it had not been found. Plans were then put in place to commission a replacement. On the following Sunday, the Feast of the Assumption, Gerry was out walking the dogs when he saw the statue under a pile of leaves.

He called Stephen Lovell and asked him to bring his car and they managed to clean it up and restore it to its rightful position. The statute still stands in the grounds of the nursing home. Who had removed it and why has always remained a mystery.

Margaret Byrne was in St Vincent's from the age of eight years until twelve years. While she was in the hospital she met Kathleen Blackaller, now Kathleen Gowan.

Father O'Daly was very good with us children and he was such fun. I remember when he used to give us our weekly dose of cod liver oil and malt (yummie), how he would hold the spoon way over our heads and we were lucky if it reached our mouths. He would lie on a spare bed and let the children cover him with flowers and weeds and he always had his dog Towser with him.

One time when the pigs from the hospital farm were going for slaughter, they were brought into the field in front of our ward. When herded together one escaped and was running round and round so it took ages to catch it.

When we didn't eat our dinners one of the walking patients would throw it over the field, but I am not sure the Sisters knew this.

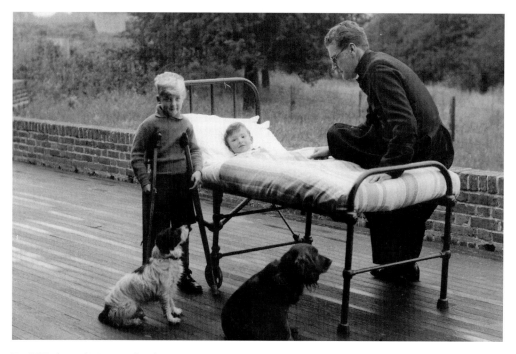

Fr O'Daly and Towser the dog.

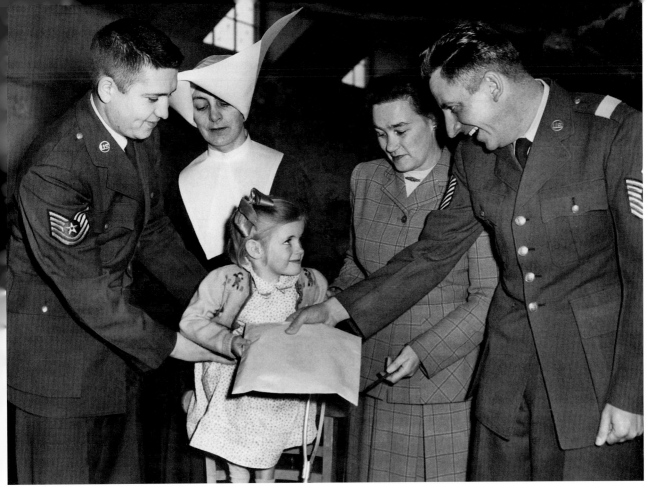

Sr Vincent Neilan, Matron, Miss Bacon, Secretary, and American soldiers.

One of the Sisters did some drawings on the wall and we asked for Roy Rogers on his horse. At Halloween we hung sheets over the beams with torches for eyes and when Sister came on her night round we all made howling sounds.

American soldiers were stationed nearby and they came to give us parties, lots of chocolates and of course chewing gum when we asked 'Got any gum chum?' My father, Mr Byrne, used to sing to us on Sundays when he visited. My memories of St Vincent's were indeed happy.

AMERICAN SOLDIERS

Kathleen Gowan also recalls American soldiers coming to visit children at Christmas and giving the children each a present; she had a brush and comb set:

At Christmas we always went around the wards singing carols and I sang on my own for one or two songs.

We were taken on many trips, once to Bertram Mills Circus but I didn't really like that very much. I preferred seeing the little piglets and their mother on the farm.

A BUTTON found on the floor of a Pinner Green shop by a detective constable investigating a robbery that had taken place there, helped trace the culprits.

Previously this had been stated in evidence against three sailors who appeared for sentence at Herts Quarter Sessions last Monday charged with breaking and entering W. H. Smith & Sons, High-street, Watford, and entering a shop in Pinner Green and stealing goods to the total value of 16s.8d.

The sailors, 21-years-old Brian Albert Johnson, 19-years-old Barry Wells, both of Frithwood Lodge, Northwood; and 24-years-old Londoner, Patrick Vincent Kinsella, pleaded guilty.

MATCHED JACKET

Det. Cons. John Seaford said at a lower court that he found a button on the floor of the shop, and on later investigation found that it matched the buttons of a suede jacket hanging behind the door of a room in which Wells and Johnson lived.

Wells was fined a total of £40, Johnson £30 and Kinsella £20.

Deputy-chairman, Mr. Frederick Crowder, MP, said that if the RN had not been willing to have them back after the case they would have gone to prison.

Proprietor of the "Clay", Mr. Jack Ingram hands a giant-sized teddy bear to nurse Comdom and nurse Kenna from St. Vincent's hospital. The teddy was given by Eastcote toy shop.

A party to remember

For children of St. Vincent's Orthopaedic Hospital, Eastcote, and a local orphanage last Tuesday afternoon was a dream come true. In the gaily decorated Clay Pigeon, Eastcote a huge party was held for them.

Toys had been collected from all over the district. American servicemen from South Ruislip helped to swell the collection for the 52 children at the party.

A film show, conjuror, sing song and a huge tea kept the children amused throughout the afternoon.

Conjuror David Ball from Northwood kept the party amused with his tricks and the film show was given by Mr. A. S. Hott, Ruislip-Northwood Road Safety Officer.

Representatives of the 1st Motor Transport Squadron, U.S.A.F. base, South Ruislip, Staff Sgt. R. Blymiller gives toys to David Page and little Kevin Goldsmith. The American presents came as a last minute extra for the children. Holding Kevin is Mr. R. Rabson of the Regal florists, Eastcote.

USAF fundraising for the children.

When it got to a point where the hospital could do no more for me I worked in the hospital laundry, while the boys worked in the workshop making boots, shoes and callipers. We all loved St Vincent's, we had some good times and used to sleep outside in the open air and have midnight snacks under the bedclothes.

Fr O'Daly and his housekeeper Agnes were great fun. He died from a chest problem following a fire in his house, the night after Cardinal Heenan had visited and given a present to every patient from a huge Christmas stocking. Fr O'Daly had said to Sr Mary Jo Powell DC. 'I have had everything now. Lourdes, Fatima and now this day!' He died in the ambulance on the way to casualty. Fr O'Daly was loved by everyone – but especially by the children.

END OF AN ERA MCCRAE AITKEN RETIRES

On 31 December 1948 the Board announced the retirement of Mr McCrae Aitken FRCS, who had been surgeon to the hospital for 38 years. He was first associated with St Vincent's at Clapham from 1910 to 1912 and came to Pinner when the boys were transferred. Mrs McCrae Aitken was also the librarian for St Vincent's for nine years.

Subscriptions and donations during the 1950s in support of St Vincent's were phenomenal.

Above: Mr McCrae Aitken FRCS (third from right) retires following 38 years' association with St Vincent's.

Left: St Paul's Ward: cake from HRH The Queen on the occasion of Prince Charles' birthday. Nurse Kenna and Sr Angela Murray (Matron) share with the boys the same age as Prince Charles.

BUILDING FUNDS

St Vincent's was a typical orthopaedic hospital in that it was spread over many acres, developing and growing in response to the demand for more specialist care and attention.

A building fund had been launched in 1949 to replace the original wooden huts. The children's ward alone was to cost in excess of £30,000, which was a significant amount of money. The fundraising began in earnest and the King Edward's Hospital Fund for London generously promised £5,000. The rebuilding started in September 1950 and the ambitious project created St Michael's Ward, St Margaret's Ward and the outpatients' waiting room.

During 1950 the hospital continued to develop and rising costs did not deter the determination to provide the best for the patients. St Michael's Ward was rebuilt and work on St Margaret's was started in 1951, along with the improvements to the outpatients' waiting room, all brick built with sliding doors to keep out the bad weather in winter.

The Board of Management clearly had their sights on ensuring the hospital developed: sterilisers were installed in each ward and in theatre; the student nurses' classroom was enlarged and improved, with the nurses' home redecorated.

STATISTICS FOR YEAR TO 31 DECEMBER 1950

Inpatients
Year

	1950	1949
1. Beds		
(a) Complement at 31 December	176	200
(b) Av. daily complement during the year	176	200
(c) Av. daily number closed during the year owing to:		
i. rebuilding or extension	–	–
ii. repairs, redecoration, cleaning or infection	–	–
iii. other causes	–	–
(d) Av. daily number open during the year	176	200
(e) Av. daily number occupied during the year	146	158
2. Number of inpatients in the hospital at the beginning of the year	140	156
3. Number of inpatients admitted during the year	428	283
4. Number of inpatients in hospital at the end of the year	128	140
5. Av. number of days each patient was resident	121	193
6. Number of patients admitted and discharged during the year who were resident:		
(a) only one day	21	8
(b) two and three days	31	25

Outpatients

Total number of new outpatients

(a) Ruislip clinic	909
(b) Hospital	1,819
Total	**2,728**

Total number of attendances

(a) Ruislip clinic	14,492
(b) Hospital	9,622
Total	**24,114**

X-ray department	3,096

Physio treatments

(a) Ruislip clinic	14,492
(b) Hospital	14,420
Total	**28,912**

Operations undertaken	398

The clinical activity during the 1950s gives an insight into the pressures and life of the community. Within the Annual Report a classification of patients treated during 1950 shares a picture of life after the war.

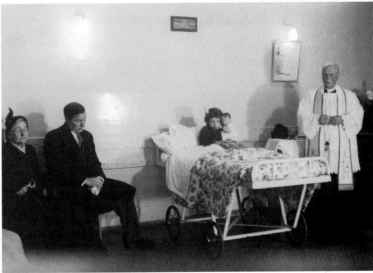

Above left: St Margaret's Ward girls.

Above right: Fr Bagnell and Carol Getgood.

CLASSIFICATION OF PATIENTS TREATED IN 1950

Tuberculosis		Fractures	
Spine	52	Fibula	7
Hip	37	Radius	7
Knee	18	Ulna	6
Ankle	5	Spine	3
Other joints	16	Humerus	4
Arthritis	30	Femur	16
Osteomyelitis	19	Tibia	17
Osteogenesis imperfecta	2		
Spondylitis	2	**Other:**	
Osteochondritis	15	Hallux valgus & rigidus	27
Anterior poliomyelitis	44	Pes planus & cavus	4
Spastic paralysis	33	Exostosis	27
Congenital dislocation hip	16	Trauma	12
Talipes equinovarus	8	Nervous system	13
Spina bifida	1	Internal Derangement of knee	23
Scoliosis	2	Medical	44
Prolapsed discs	22		

AFTER-CARE CLINICS

The most striking difference between work at St Vincent's Hospital, which dealt with the rehabilitation of the crippled, and a hospital where cases of disease and injury in patients of all ages are admitted is remarkable.

Aftercare clinics were centres where patients under the care of the hospital, but not at the time in need of inpatient treatment, could come for a periodic overhaul.

The clinical appointment would re-examine the notes on their case sheet and brought them up to date, their apparatus was reviewed, and any necessary alterations or repairs put in hand, fresh instructions were given to the patients' parents or attendants and a review was made of their future course. At these clinics, fresh cases which have been referred from the neighbourhood with a recommendation for admission to St Vincent's were also examined and passed for acceptance or referred to some other centre.

The clinics were held wherever a group of patients resided, usually in hospitals central to the district or a building providing necessary accommodation. The number of sessions at each clinic varied with the number of patients in a district. In some a monthly visit attended by a surgeon, Matron and Aftercare Sister filled all the requirements, in others the Aftercare Sister held her own inspection at intermediate times, overlooking plasters and apparatus, and sorting out those who needed to be seen at the next full clinic.

Voluntary Aid Detachment (VAD) nurses would regularly assist at the many clinics to ensure patients had help with their treatment.

One young boy who came to St Vincent's during the 1950s was Anthony Rapley, a patient on Holy Child Ward. His sister, Margaret Tobin, recounts her visits and Anthony's life there.

Tony Rapley developed polio at the age of six months in 1948 when there was a major epidemic in London.

Initially he had been in Queen Mary's Hospital, Carshalton, the large children's hospital serving South London.

Realising that Tony would be hospitalised for some years and wishing him to be cared for in a Catholic environment, my mother arranged for his transfer to St Vincent's. She was a friend from Scotland of Sr Angela, then the Sister tutor for the nursing staff.

Tony came to St Vincent's in 1950 aged 2 and remained until 1954.

Mother was determined that Tony would know he was part of a family, so my parents and I made the long journey every Sunday from South London to St Vincent's. We had no car and the journey entailed three trains and a taxi from Northwood Hills station.

Tony's ward was run by Nurse Kenna, who became his surrogate mother and whom he loved very much.

Above left: Anthony Rapley on a standing frame, 1953.

Above right: Anthony Rapley and his sister Margaret in the garden of St Vincent's, 1952.

Sr Mary Joseph Powell DC at storytime in 1959. Elizabeth is the girl on the right with glasses. The blonde girl is Dilys Jones.

The ward was open on one side and the boys' beds were pushed outside onto the wooden decking. My mother often sat with the other boy patients on the ward, as some appeared to have no family visits.

We also visited the Chapel each week with Tony. I recall the Annual Garden Fetes each August was great fun. I vividly remember Sr Angela taking me into her classroom to introduce me to her skeleton that she used in teaching the nurses.

St Vincent's was a great influence on me and I eventually became a nurse myself.

A patient in 1950, Elizabeth Greeley is an example of one girl's determination to be able to live her life accepting that, in spite of the severest disability, she knows what a loving God means.

She lives with cerebral palsy and has found the strength to make a life that is as rewarding as any other despite the extreme difficulties of the condition and the prejudices of society.

Liz came to St Vincent's when she was four years old, as she was too disabled to live at home. Sr Mary Jo Powell DC, known at the time as Sr Joseph, took Liz under her wing and ensured that her five years at the hospital were as homely as possible.

Liz's family lived in Huddersfield but they visited monthly and her mother wrote and sent a parcel every Wednesday – a day that was to become a very special part of the week.

One incident that Liz recalls was when the ice cream van called on the ward and all the children wanted an ice cream. Liz did not have any money but knew that her father was coming that afternoon and would give her the twopence she needed for the ice cream. Liz therefore thought it would be okay for her to 'borrow' twopence from Sister's desk, knowing she could put it back later.

However, Liz was caught by the nurse when she was returning the twopence and was therefore in trouble and unable to go to Communion that day until she had been to Confession. Liz recalls being very upset about the situation because she had every intention of returning the money. The incident has stayed with her – and fortunately her father could see the predicament and would often tease her about it years later.

Liz has had a remarkable life managing with her condition, which causes involuntary movement, often rendering her unable to use her voice audibly, and has led to major problems in swallowing.

She has dedicated her life to helping other disabled children and in 1986 Liz Greeley was awarded the British Empire Medal for her work. She has since spoken to hundreds of people, giving encouragement and hope.

The children started taking tests in shorthand and typing from 1951 and continued to be awarded scholarships.

The local paper as keen to support the children and news of good academic and achievement was always welcome.

A new dairy was built on the farm and later an electric milking machine was added. That year the Annual Garden Fete raised £1,000.

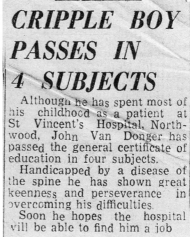

CRIPPLE BOY PASSES IN 4 SUBJECTS

Although he has spent most of his childhood as a patient at St Vincent's Hospital, Northwood, John Van Donger has passed the general certificate of education in four subjects.

Handicapped by a disease of the spine he has shown great keenness and perseverance in overcoming his difficulties.

Soon he hopes the hospital will be able to find him a job

Above left: Elizabeth Greeley receives her British Empire Medal.

Above right: John Van Donger passes four subjects in the General Certificate of Education while at St Vincent's.

Left: Children enjoying the sunshine; Sr Kevin Thompson replaces Sr Josephine as headteacher in 1947.

Below: St Paul's Ward, 1951. Left to right: Ronnie, Jojo, Mickey, Gordon, Tom, John.

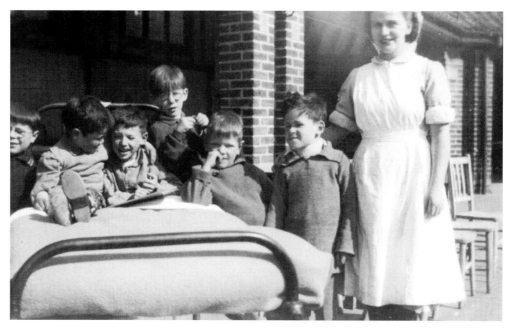

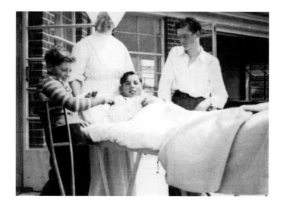

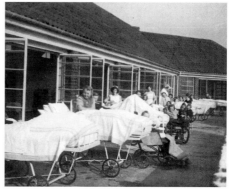

Above left: Sr Elizabeth DC and Gerry Smith (standing) on the St Paul's Ward patio.

Above right: Sr Joseph Powell DC and the staff at the new St Margaret's Ward nursery.

LOURDES PILGRIMAGES

The children were able to join the annual trips to Lourdes, being prepared, and packed and assigned a buddy. They were escorted by Nurse Kenna and a number of other nurse assistants, then the Sisters would see them off, as they did not accompany the children.

Judith Hawkins tells of when her brother Philip was admitted in 1952 at the age of five with poliomyelitis affecting one knee: 'He was a patient on St Paul's Ward with all those boys who had been there for so long. Johnny Sheehan's legs were all crumpled but he swung expertly around his cot.'

Years later, she met Johnny again, he'd had his legs amputated and sped around the hospital grounds in his wheelchair. Johnny was employed in the workshops – St Vincent's was always his home.

Philip was a patient for several months on bed rest and was later fitted with a calliper and special boots, made in the hospital workshops, so he could get about again.

Above: Judith and Philip Hawkins and their mum.

Top right: The boys on the move: the boy being pushed by the nurse has hydrocephalus.

Bottom right: Taking 'first steps': Mrs Carr in the hospital gymnasium.

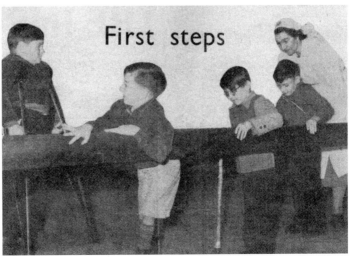

Above: Boys working together.

Left: Older boys on the move. Note the calliper.

Below: Happy days! Boys for the camera.

The ward was right at the lower end of the hospital grounds overlooking fields with sheep and cattle, part of the hospital farm. Philip was taught by one of the Sisters. Nurse Kenna was so kind to us all, Philip, my mother and father and me.

I used to visit the shop close to the ward, a wooden building. Selling teas and cakes and I remember with relish the aniseed balls! I recall seeing rosaries for sale and wanting my mother to buy me one, such a pretty 'necklace' and she did.

There were large canvas sheets hanging across the ward where windows would have been. Nearly always folded away to allow in air, wind and sometimes snow; the patients were open to the elements and that healing fresh air. Philip recovered from polio but has not forgotten his time on St Paul's Ward.

Miss Kenna lived into her 90s but during her youth had been associated with St Vincent's for 21 years, working caring for sick children as a nurse. Miss Kenna's father when only a young man of 36 years a captain in the 21st Lancers (Empress of India's) British Army during the Sudan campaign was awarded the Victoria Cross for his courage in the Battle of Omdurman. He also competed in the 1912 Summer Olympics for Great Britain as a horse rider, which was the first time equestrian events were held.

He did not finish the Individual Eventing (military) competition, and the British team did not finish the team event. In the individual jumping event he finished 27th. Miss Kenna was an only child and died in 1998.

Above left: St Paul's Ward, on the verandah.

Above right: St Paul's Ward. Note the callipers.

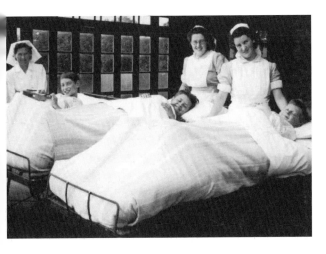 

Above left: St Paul's Ward: bed boys.

Above right: Left to right: Rev. John Bebb, Chaplain; Miss Kenna, retiring; and Sr Genevieve Bergen DC.

Miss Kenna had written some of her fondest memories of St Vincent's, which are reflected here.

Mr McCrae Aitken was an eminent surgeon of the day who took great interest in the children living in St Vincent's. One summer afternoon, to my utter astonishment, Mr McCrae Aitken appeared entirely on his own on St Paul's Ward.

This in itself was significant as surgeons even today rarely appear on a ward without their surgical team to assist and discuss medical matters.

However, he had come to see the 'two little polios' who had been admitted from the isolation hospital that morning. He had a look at them and then sat down on the low wall, presumably to rest before walking up the hill again.

A little group of 'up boys' (those were lads who could walk about with crutches or on their trolleys) gathered around him and he proceeded to recite nursery rhymes to them in French. 'Oomperty Doomperty assi sur un mur, Oomperty Doomperty tombe par terre' and so on.

The children were spellbound – and so was I – and if the boys did not know French they certainly recognised Humpty Dumpty, and I always like to think Mr McCrae Aitken enjoyed this little scene too!

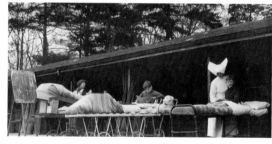

Above: St Michael's Ward before the rebuild, 1950s.

Top left: Mayor of Wembley's visit in the 1950s. Left to right: Nurse Byrne, Fr Galvin, Mayor of Wembley, Sr Mary (Matron), Miss Bacon (Secretary), Miss Kenna and the boys.

Bottom left: Fr Galvin, Mayor of Wembley, Sr Mary Neville DC and Miss Bacon at the official opening of St Michael's Ward, 1952.

The story of St. Vincent's Orthopaedic Hospital, Eastcote

THE IMPOSSIBLE TAKES LONGER

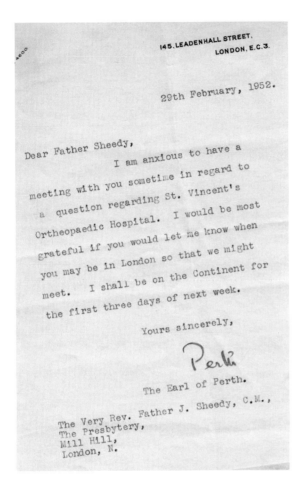

145. LEADENHALL STREET,
LONDON, E.C.3.

29th February, 1952.

Dear Father Sheedy,

I am anxious to have a meeting with you sometime in regard to a question regarding St. Vincent's Orthopaedic Hospital. I would be most grateful if you would let me know when you may be in London so that we might meet. I shall be on the Continent for the first three days of next week.

Yours sincerely,

Perth

The Earl of Perth.

The Very Rev. Father J. Sheedy, C.M.,
The Presbytery,
Mill Hill,
London, N.

Above: A local paper, *The Post*, produces a three-page spread about St Vincent's in December 1953. The headline is: 'The Impossible Takes Longer', taken from the American Strategic Air Command motto from the Second World War: 'The extremely difficult we do at once – the impossible takes a little longer.'

Left: Correspondence from the Earl of Perth to Fr Sheedy (Chaplain).

Below: Sr Elizabeth on St Michael's Ward. Note the new French windows.

By 1954 all the wooden wards had been replaced with brick and had glass sliding doors which could be closed if necessary.

Sister Rosalie was a Daughter of Charity in Pinner from 1955 to 1967 and by the time she left there was a lovely new Chapel, babies' ward and a Sisters' House.

In the early days seven older Sisters slept in the rooms above the Matron's Office, two Sisters in the huts on the edge of the woods, one of which was the night sister, and the rest slept in cubicles at the ends of the wards to be near the children.

I remember sleeping at the end of St Teresa's Ward, sharing with Sr Gerard. One hot summer night we had the window wide open and I was awoken by loud snoring. I thought it was Sr Gerard and I suppose she thought it was me, however upon looking around, I realised that it was a big pig that roamed in from the field and had fallen asleep under our window!

When my family heard I was in charge of the hospital laundry they must have laughed, as I hadn't got a clue, but I had good staff and I learned the hard way by my mistakes. We said the Angelus at every midday and one of my staff thought we said, 'May the Divine Sisters remain always with us' instead of 'may the Divine assistance'.

The Sisters' refectory backed onto the male workers' refectory, former air-raid shelters, where lots of wild cats meandered around. When Sr Kevin took the food scraps out to the pig bins she would usually throw some to the cats.

One night she was heard to say to the cats, 'Don't be around tomorrow, pussies, they are coming to get you.' When the men came the next day with nets and cages there wasn't a cat to be seen.

The hardware stores were given out by the kitchen Sister. Sr Gerard Burns went to collect her stores one day and there was 'one lavatory brush' on the list. 'What do you want that for?' asked Sister Augustine. 'To clean my teeth!'

In the early days a little Glaswegian boy asked Sr Kevin if they could have the hymn with 'lace on' it when Sr Kevin couldn't recall it, he sang, 'kyrie e-e-e-e-leison'.

CHRISTMASTIME

On Christmas Day the Sisters served dinner on the wards, in the nurses' home, in the men's home and in the Domestic Home. Only after this did the Sisters have their own Christmas dinner! They only lit the fire in the community room at Christmas, and on 28 December the young Sisters presented a concert for older Sisters.

Christmas was always a time of great joy within the hospital and gifts of all kinds were showered on the hospital in great abundance.

Gerry Smith recalls: 'We used to look forward to the fancy dress party at Christmas. Nurses, Miss Kenna and Byrne dressed as the Toni twins: grey skirts, white blouses and a curly cover on their heads.

'Mrs Ferguson went as the "sack look", she had cut holes for her head and arms in a black bag she had a smart hat and swaggered round with a walking stick, it was such fun. When Miss Kenna put on "Snow White and the Seven Dwarfs", one dwarf was a little Down's syndrome boy – he lost all interest in his part when the cows came into the field, and he just went to the window.'

At Christmas groups went around the wards in fancy dress from the nurses' party, Everest climbers, space men. Men voted for their own Jesus and made a crown of thorns. The Sisters did music and direction.

Top: There is a carnival atmosphere on St Margaret's Ward on Christmas Day during the late 1950s. Here you can see Sr Joseph Powell DC and Nurse Celeste Bowe.

Above left: Christmas beds.

Above right: Christmas on St Theresa's Ward in 1953 with Sr Gertrude Heery DC.

Left: Christmas on St Paul's Ward.

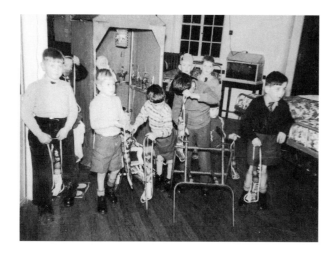

Left: Christmas stockings.

Below left: Christmas in the 1950s: Sr Gertrude DC, otherwise known as Sr Jane Heery DC, later went to the missions in Ethiopia.

Below right: Home for Christmas.

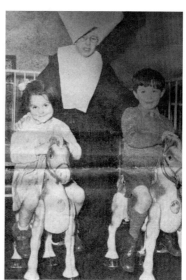

There was no TV, only the Queen's speech at 3pm.

What turned out to be a hospital joke started like this. During the war over-heard during a night air-raid: one ARP warden said to another, 'Is everything all right?' 'Yes,' was the reply, 'a bomb fell in the hen-run but the Cockerels are put-ting it out'.

True, because the Cockerels were two brothers in the ARP!!

1953 was a somewhat quiet year, although the new radio equipment was installed.

By 1953 the weekly cost per patient rose to £10 5s 5d.

ONE DAY DURING THE 1950S

Sr Mary Jo Powell and George were clearing out a storeroom and found some props for the Passion play called 'No Greater Love', George tells us.

Sr Mary Jo became the director, stage manager and adviser and, with a number of men from the hospital, and Sr Mary Jo convincing some of the female staff, we soon had a great cast with a lot of acting talent.

We were all nationalities and with so many languages being spoken we laughed and said it seemed we were 'speaking in tongues'.

Sr Mary Jo's calm nature was very inspiring and we all behaved so well during rehearsals. Staff, men and women used the empty hall for rehearsals. The play was so successful it ran for three nights with a full house every evening. Sr Anthony, who ran the sweet shop in the canteen, ran out of sweets because she gave them all away.

The men made shields with silver paper and dustbin lids. Mr Hagan from the tailors' shop lent red flannel (used for lining nurses' cloaks) for Roman soldiers/ centurions and the nurses made costumes and 'Eastern' veils from old covers. Gerry Smith and the team did the lighting and sound effects - it was great!!

The ending of a Passion play is difficult, so we had all the players, women, soldiers and children around Jesus on the cross – then a complete blackout and we played the 'Hallelujah Chorus' timed to the minute – then all the lights on … and Jesus saying Mass as a man in modern dress and all the players as SAS soldiers or police dressed in modern clothes. A thrilling finish!!!

Another production 'Frost over Pinner', ridiculing each department, was very funny. Then the 'International Show' had each person doing a national dance or representation. England did Buckingham Palace with a real corgi.

Passion play.

Children dressing up.

Also the song 'Puppet on a String' with a tall nurse dressed in a Union Jack and a very small nurse as a ballerina – on strings. One nurse went home to Wales to collect her national costume!

It was said of St Vincent's in 1953:

> You may not notice the difference as you walk up the hill, along the winding lane and past the hospital farm. It may not strike you until you are well inside the hospital gates. But sooner or later you will agree with all who know St Vincent's well - it is a world apart.
>
> You need no password to enter. You are not asked to conform with their ways and become a Catholic but you do begin to understand the meaning of faith.

One man who worked in the workshops for many years said, 'I am not a Catholic, I suppose I would not be called a religious man, but I have learned something of the meaning and effect of faith since I have been here'.

Another reportedly said:

> The Sisters are unbelievable. Whenever they are faced with the impossible, which is quite often in their type of work, they go and pray. They don't rely on prayer to bring about miracles but to give them strength to work that much harder. They never spare themselves. They never seem to worry, and always seem to be working.

Not until you appreciate the spirit of these Sisters can you begin to know St Vincent's. Their cheerfulness and courage, inspires patients, nurses, doctors, and all who work at St Vincent's.

Meanwhile improvements were being made very frequently in all departments. Central heating had been installed in parts of the hospital. St Vincent's can be credited as a pioneer of occupational therapy: staff and trainees made the majority of surgical appliances, clothes and uniforms, and could repair and extend many of the buildings. During 1955 there were 176 beds with babies admitted as required.

From the age of 13, the education of a child was combined with practical instruction in the workshops. In this way they were able to make the fullest use of their hands, defeat their fear of being 'useless' and gain confidence to acquire further skills.

Above left: The Old Boys' Association put on many plays, and here is the cast of one such performance.

Above right: Everyone gets involved, including the Chaplain.

Left: Nurses take a break on St Vincent's Ward.

Above left: Miss Olive Bacon, Company Secretary.

Abov centre: Miss Bacon, Mr Sayer and Mr Russell, both Old Boys.

Above right: Pat and Lusi, administrative staff.

Right: Tiny.

Many patients found full-time employment after their training at St Vincent's and others built up businesses of their own.

Sr Vincent Neilan DC was both superintendent and Matron, and many of the Sisters had key roles within the hospital. Day-to-day administration was carried out by laypeople. Miss Olive Bacon was hospital secretary.

Miss Bacon came to St Vincent's in 1943 as a telephone operator and to type letters for the hospital secretary. She completed the Hospital Administrators' Diploma in 1948 and retired in 1981 when Anthony Janssens was Chairman.

Mr J. Laffey (bedridden for five years) and Mr H. Raciti (eight years' treatment) were ex-patients who successfully ran the accounts department. They worked at St Vincent's and helped everyone and were very popular. Many other ex-patients stayed on, like James Naylor, who was stone deaf but was a remarkable and fine craftsman, making complicated surgical appliances in the metal shop.

The workshop made splints for places as far afield as Dagenham, Barnet, Peckham and Harefield.

Albert Richardson and Lithuanian Peter Diegutus served 50 years between them, working wonders with leather to make boots and shoes. Orders came from hospitals miles around for such items as raised shoes.

Mr Con Hopley, who managed the bootmaking and repairing department, worked at the hospital for 30 years, having been a patient for three years as a young lad.

Bill Quinn, one of his assistants who spent five years in bed with TB spine, worked at St Vincent's all his life and was also the scout master for St Vincent's Scouts, later helping out with the Northwood Troop.

William Hagan was manager of the tailors' workshop and one of his apprentices was Gerry Smith who stayed working at the hospital until it closed in 1999. Mr Hagan taught many of the lads and his workshop made clothes for the young patients and staff and surgical clothes for the doctors and nurses.

Sr Agnes was busy in the workroom (together with budgerigars and a white canary), making and repairing bed linen and new garments for Sisters and patients.

The farm bailiff in 1955 was Mr A.G. Perry, who took up his position in 1939. Al Staines looked after the engineering of the hospital for 30 years. Guy Perry took responsibility for about 100 pigs, over 300 head of poultry and milking 15 cows. Three-quarters of the hospital's milk consumption, about 40 gallons a day, came from the farms, so did hundreds of eggs and about 140lbs of home-killed pork or veal a week. There were also 200 pigs a year sold to raise funds.

Top left: Mr Docherty in the workshop, guiding one of the senior boys.

Centre left: Mr Hopley provides instruction to Joseph Daly, aged 14, Arthur Dooland, aged 14, and Teddy Wilson, aged 16.

Bottom left: The boot shop: children busy making the shoes and splints.

Below: Mr Hopley in the boot shop.

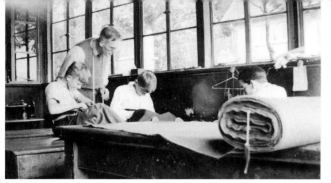

Above: William Hagan supervising in the tailors' workshop.

Left: Girls busy toy-making. Note the calliper.

Below: Willy Whitehorn up on his feet.

PAIR OF CRUTCHES WAS HIS FINEST CHRISTMAS GIFT

BIGGEST STORY EVER IN THE POST

Willie Whitehorn had never walked. During the six years of his life he had never once stood on his feet. Three years ago he came to St. Vincent's Hospital, Eastcote, and a few days before Christmas this year he stood for the first time—the best Christmas present anyone ever had

Weekly Post Editor says: 'In my opinion we publish today the finest story ever written for this newspaper.'

TURN TO PAGES 7, 8, 9, 10

RT IN
-EVER
MAS

TER

e roads during the holiday
tmas for many years for
han 20 cars were involved
in hospital suffering from
everal people are nursing

hristmas occurred outside
in fog on Wednesday and
the cars were damaged but,
eriously injured.
"queue-up" collision ever
nue—started at 8.50 a.m. and
volved until 9.45 a.m. Only
rs. I. Berens, of Chalfont St.

AMERICAN BASE OPENS NEW HOSPITAL

The new U.S.A.F. hospital that has been under construction for three years was opened at the South Ruislip American Base last Monday. Lt. General William H. Tunner, C-in-C, U.S.A.F. forces in Europe and Air Marshal Sir

MAIL WAS BIGGER THAN EVER

Harrow Post Office covering also the Ruislip - Northwood area, handled a record number of 4,713,614 letters and post cards during the Christmas mail rush. Overall figures show an increase of six per cent on last year.

Harrow Post master, Mr. G. Buy, said that parcels and packages were packed better than ever before. He thanked the public for their co-operation in posting early. On the peak day, Monday, Dec. 21, 932,594 items were handled. The Postmaster General, Earl de la Warr was at Harrow on Monday to see the record post.

CAR STOLEN

A car belonging to Mr. Brimacombe, 15 Kewferry-road, Northwood, was taken from the car park at Green-lane, Northwood, during Wednesday night. This is the second theft from the car park within two weeks.

Sister Francis had been at St Vincent's over 30 years and was seen as a 'jack of all trades'. Apart from her clinical photography she took many other photographs over the years and was also related to the famous photographic family of Bailey.

Sister Francis also ran the tuck shop and in her spare time liked to do model-making.

Catherine Carr was for 35 years responsible for supervising the various types of massage, exercise and electrical treatments for the children. Working alongside Mrs McNeale and other nurses, they taught hundreds of patients how to walk, often for the first time or for the first time in many years.

Willy Whitehorn had never walked during his six years, nor once been on his feet, but after three years at St Vincent's he stood for the first time.

The hospital had its own farm, fresh creamy milk, and large double yoked eggs stay in my mind. The food was quite repetitive as we only had what was in season.

Sweets were treats but we had some at Christmas and at Easter a huge chocolate egg was donated. Miss Pat, who looked after the domestic duties, would make the most delicious hot chocolate with some of this thick chocolate egg.

Above left: Janet Arnold and Frank Kelland.

Above centre: Easter, 1956. The secretaries left to right: Miss Carrasto, Miss Bacon and Miss Foster. (Donated by Ward, Sharp and sons Ltd.)

Above right: David Carter, 9 years old, holds the gigantic Easter Egg.

Above left: Children share an Easter egg.

Top right: Easter time and the anticipation.

Centre right, bottom right: Children playing.

Below left: Captain Formby and Miss Bacon, 1957.

It was a sad year for St Vincent's in 1957 when it suffered the loss of three important lives. Richard Stokes, the dynamic Chairman of the Board of Management was killed in a road accident. Chaplain Fr O'Daly died after a fire in his flat, and the lady who collected the subscriptions for the Old Boys' Association also died.

Captain Formby succeeded as Chairman of the Board and progress continued. The combined efforts of the workshops were taking a gross amount well in excess of £4,000 annually but the weekly cost per patient rose sharply to £12 5s 2d.

— INTO THE 1960s —

By 1959 all wards had their own television sets, most were gifts to the hospital. The financial situation at the hospital happily improved and in 1960 the Regional Health Authority now paid the full cost of the NHS patients.

The calculations for the national pay awards was very different during the 1950s and it depended on the size of the hospital and also the age of the staff. Board and lodgings were also stipulated nationally.

Many people continued to benefit from the excellent care within St Vincent's into what for many was the 'Swinging Sixties'.

The health of the nation had improved dramatically by the 1960s and this was reflected in the nature of patient care at St Vincent's. There was better food and housing, indoor sanitation and heating, together with the Clean Air Act and employment benefits.

Tuberculosis was no longer a scourge in the UK due to the pasteurisation of milk, the mass chest X-ray scheme, BCG vaccination and effective TB drugs, such as streptomycin, PAS and INAH. Vaccination effectively eradicated poliomyelitis, while penicillin tackled impending osteomyelitis.

Rickets became a thing of the past and congenital deformities could be corrected earlier, so the need for long-term inpatient child care gradually diminished.

Meanwhile, a fitter, longer-lived older population developed degenerative arthritic diseases. Orthopaedic care moved into prosthetic hip and knee replacement surgery, facilitated by improved surgical procedures and radiography and the availability of antibiotics. The weekly cost per patient had risen sharply to £17 1s 4d.

In 1960 a novel type of physiotherapy appeared at the hospital in the form of a gift of a retired circus pony. Children were taught exercises while riding him and their otherwise tight leg muscles with spastic paralysis were quite relaxed while they were in the saddle. Riding for the disabled has subsequently grown to be recognised as a worthy form of exercise and joy for disadvantaged children.

N.M.C Circular No. 79   22 April 1959

Grade	Salary Scale	Increments	Board and Lodging charge where resident
Matron (Training School)	£		£
1,000 beds & over	1,325 – 1,565	45(2) 50	360
700-999 beds	1,225 - 1,450	(3)	315
500-699 beds	1,125 – 1,335	45 (5)	290
300-499 beds	1,035 - 1,235	40(3) 45(2)	285
200-299 beds	965 - 1,150	40 (5)	285
100-199 beds	915 - 1,075	35(3)	285
Under 100 beds	875 – 1,025	40(2)	275
		30(3)	
		35(2)	
		30 (5)	
Matron (Non Training School)			
500-699 beds	965 - 1,150	35(3)	275
300-499 beds	915 - 1,075	40(2)	270
200-299 beds	875 – 1,025	30(3)	270
100-199 beds		35(2)	265
Under 100 beds		30 (5)	265
		30 (5)	
		30 (4)	
Matron (Training School)			
500 beds and over	835 – 955	30 (4)	240
300-499 beds	805 - 925	30 (4)	240
200-299 beds	775 - 895	30 (4)	235
Under 200 beds	750 - 870	30 (4)	230
Matron (Non Training School)			
500 beds and over	805 - 925	30 (4)	240
300-499 beds	775 - 895	30 (4)	235
Under 300 beds	750 - 870	30 (4)	230
Nursing Assistant			
Age 20	320		128
Age 19	300		128
Age 18	285		128
	Salary per 4 hour session		
Ward Sister	23s.4d		
Staff Nurse	17s. 11d		
Enrolled Nurse Assistant	15s. 4d		
Nursing Auxillary 21 yrs and over	13s.11d		
Nursing Auxillary 20 yrs	9s.6d		
Nursing Auxillary 19 yrs	8s 9d		
Nursing Auxillary 18 yrs	8s 3d		

No charge shall be made for meals on taken on duty or for use and laundering of uniform.

Nurses' salaries, 1959.

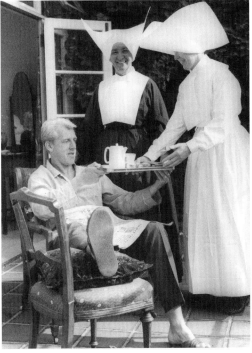

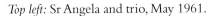

Top left: Sr Angela and trio, May 1961.

Above: Lord and Lady Vansittart opening the 1952 horse show (with Miss Bacon and Fr O'Daly).

Top right: Ian Ure, Scotland and Arsenal football player, Sr Angela DC and Sr Mary DC, Ward Sister.

Centre right, above: Local riders join in the horse show in 1955. The wards can be seen in the background.

Centre right, below: Gymkhana at St Vincent's.

Bottom right: Fundraising at the gymkhana.

Top: The Irish ambassador and his wife meet the twins and Miss Kenna.

Above: A pony at one of the horse shows.

Right: Booklet for St Vincent's Horse Show and Gymkhana.

Schedule of the . . .

ST. VINCENT'S
ORTHOPÆDIC HOSPITAL
4th ANNUAL

Horse Show
and Gymkhana

(Affiliated to B.H.S., H.I.S., B.S.J.A., B.S.P.S.)

WILL BE HELD AT

EASTCOTE PINNER, MIDDX.

Saturday, September 10, 1955

COMMENCING AT 10 A.M.

★

Judges:		Classes
Mrs. N. Howe	..	1, 2, 4, 6, 7,
C. J. H. Gale, Esq., M.R.C.V.S.	...	3, 5, 9.
D. W. Mould, Esq. ...	...	3, 4, 9.
T. C. Parker, Esq. ...	...	5, 7, 8.
E. T. Teunus, Esq. ..	...	1, 2, 6, 8.
Capt. C. F. Platts ...	...	10, 11, 12, 13.

Hon. Secretary:

Miss E. C. Brooks, 11 Napier Road, Wembley, Middx.
Tel.: Wembley 4848

The farm was now supplying all the hospital's requirement in milk and eggs, with surplus milk sold to the Milk Marketing Board and surplus eggs to visitors.

Two student nurses took first and fifth place in the orthopaedic examination for the whole of Great Britain.

Fundraising was a constant theme within St Vincent's and the 1960s decade started with a wonderful Gala Ball where all proceeds went to the hospital.

They did not win—but these lovelies made this contest possible

IT is six years since the Weekly Post launched its first Gala Queen Contest. In that time it has grown until it is now recognised as one of the major competitions if its kind in the South of England.

The success of this contest is due to the many lovely local girls who are prepared to enter. There has never been a shortage of entrants, partly because of the attractive prizes offered, but mostly because Middlesex is blessed with an abundance of beautiful girls who are prepared to enter into the spirit of the competition. Winners and losers throughout all the preliminary rounds and in the final, have displayed not only their physical charms but also their good sportsmanship—a quality not always associated with contests of this kind.

On this page are the pictures of the finalists. To them, and to those who were not so successful this year, the Post offers its sincere thanks. And the reminder that the contest will be back again in 1960.

Newspaper report of the Gala Ball.

Above left: Souvenir programme with Kay Jocelyn, aged 19.

Above right: George Bhati and his family.

As a young man in 1960 George Bhati arrived from India with a friend whose mother lived in Eastcote, and he stayed with them for a while. George recounts his experience at St Vincent's.

Shortly after arriving in England my friend's mother became ill and went to hospital. I needed accommodation and approached Mrs Schmidt, the housekeeper to our parish priest Fr Langdale at St Thomas More. He invited me to stay in the parish house (32 Field End Road), where I lived for 18 months. The house had six bedrooms two sitting rooms and a very large garden with an orchard.

During the evenings I went to Headstone School in North Harrow to improve my English and I helped in the garden and with the housework in my spare time. The bishop decided to demolish the house because of its state of disrepair and to have a smaller house built so then I needed to find elsewhere to live.

I had a job at a local garage as a motor fitter and my wages weren't much, but I only had to pay for my food. I felt lonely with no other young people around. I had heard about St Vincent's Hospital, which was run by nuns, and Fr Langdale knew Sr Angela the Matron, so it was arranged that I could stay at the hospital. I am indebted to Sr Angela Murray and Sr Joseph (now known as Sr Mary Jo Powell) and also to Arthur Stamp who looked after me and worked at the hospital.

Sr Mary Jo made me very welcome and introduced me to my room and the other men in the men's home. They included: Bill Quinn, Archie Calie, Michael O'Brien, Peter Green, John Goth, Tommy Hall, Gerry Smith, John Goff, Mr Laffey, Tony Nee, Tom Bogen, Gerry Redgrave, John Gilburt, a lad called Donald and, of course, Harry Errington. Some of these men worked on the farm and others in the hospital.

During the first night I did not sleep well but got up to go to Mass which was at 7.15 daily. Not many people were there, some workers, nurses and Sisters, who wore very large white hats and looked like angels.

The light was shining through the window and I remembered the Gospel story of the disciples walking with Jesus on the road to Emmaus – I felt happy and peaceful.

Sunday Mass was very different as the Chapel was full with many local people who came from around the area. Terry Eagar was the altar server that day, assisting Fr John Bebb the Chaplain. I also became an altar server. Terry and I became good friends.

I settled down very quickly and continued to work in the garage, also helping in the hospital especially on Sundays. I would help Miss Kenna bring the children from the wards to Mass. On two evenings I helped Sr Barbara to clean and polish the sewing room.

On occasions I was the driver for the Sisters who wanted to go too their Mother house in Mill Hill and I would drive them to the airport when required.

I did think of India sometimes and I missed my home and family, but I was happy at St Vincent's. When my father died I went home and on my return I asked Matron, Sr Vincent, if I could work full time at the hospital because I wanted to repay the kindness shown to me.

St Vincent's also introduced me to my wife, a nurse from the children's ward where Sr Pauline was in charge. I asked the young nurse to go out with me to a parish dance and we fell in love. We were married at St Matthew's, the local parish church, by Fr John Bebb and we have four wonderful children. I am still in touch with the Sisters today and I thank them for their help and always pray for St Vincent's. God Bless the Daughters of Charity wherever they may be.

CHANGING HABITS

While the habit worn by the Sisters made them appear rather formidable people, they were obviously ready for any occasion, and in fact, full of fun and the motherly love that is so important to the young.

Above left: Nuns in their white starched cornetts.

Above right: Close-up of the cornett.

Left: Daughters of Charity outside the Sisters' House at St Vincent's, 1960s.

Daughters of Charity Sr Theodora DC and Sr Angela Murray DC embrace the revised habit.

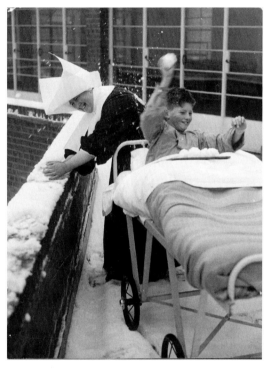

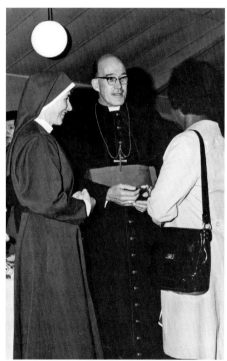

Above left: Sr Kevin Thompson, headmistress.

Above right: Sr Genevieve Bergin, Matron, and Bishop Mahon, in the 1960s. This photograph shows the refreshed habit worn by the Daughters of Charity during the 1960s.

After 1960 the headgear for Sisters diminished in size and complexity until it was completely abolished, just as happened to caps and uniforms for lay nurses. Today the Daughters of Charity choose simple everyday wear in navy, blue or grey.

The battle for change commenced in 1961 but eventually took place on 27 September 1964. Gone are the cornetts, the headgear that had to be washed, starched, and pressed into shape by its owner, and gone are the ankle-length habits.

Many Sisters choose not to wear a headdress now; however, a simple veil is worn as a mode of choice for those who do continue to wear a headdress.

ORDER OF DAY (1968)

Rise	5.50am
Meditation	6.15
Lauds	6.45
Holy Mass	7.00
Breakfast	7.45
Examen and dinner	1.00pm
Recreation	2.00
Spiritual Reading	2.30
Evening Meditation	6.30
Supper	7.00
Recreation	8.15
Compline	9.10

DAUGHTERS OF CHARITY

The Daughters of Charity celebrated the centenary of the foundation of the British Province in 1985.

In the early 1980s there were sixteen Sisters living in the community and they had a strong presence within St Vincent's, five of these Sisters, including the Matron, were employed directly in the day-to-day work of the hospital. They set the standards and created the ethos of happiness and proficiency noted by patients and staff.

Sr Joseph Powell DC was appointed as the Sister Superior of the community of Daughters of Charity, in succession to Sr Josephine Kelly, who moved to community work in Edmonton.

Sr Mary Jo DC, as she is known, retired to Pinner after a very full and active life as a Daughter of Charity. She has been a DC for over 60 years! During that time she has touched many hearts and influenced many minds and supported possibly thousands of individuals to follow their dream and ambition.

As a qualified orthopaedic nurse she was well suited to the challenges of St Vincent's in the old days and, being of good Yorkshire stock, was robust enough to ensure things were done in good order and to a high standard. Sr Mary Jo has a fabulous sense of humour and is a wonderful storyteller and will have you sitting on the edge of your seat for the next line.

Above left: Sr Joseph Powell DC, now known as Sr Mary Jo DC.

Above right: Sr Anne Remen DC and Sr Joseph Powell DC.

The Daughters of Charity clearly saw her talent and she worked as a ward Sister, and then retrained as a radiographer and worked in the Royal Free, Gray's Inn Road. Then she came to Pinner, where she worked with Sr Francis Bailey DC, the sister of the famous photographer David Bailey. The Bailey family had a passion for people which was shared and their East End beginnings ensured a robustness that endured during the challenges of St Vincent's history.

Sr Francis taught Sr Mary Jo many elements of radiography, and Sr Mary Jo also worked in Ladbroke Terrace in a private hospital for two years as a radiographer and ran the department.

After this time, there was a spell doing parish work as a parish Sister in Deptford, Wapping in the East End of London and there was a period when she worked tirelessly for six years with homeless men at the Passage, Carlisle Place, Victoria, before moving back to St Vincent's as the Sister servant.

Sr Mary Jo is a great reader and loves a 'good mystery'. She is happily retired as a resident at the nursing home in Pinner and feels her life has come full circle and is totally devoted to Our Lord and her Sisters, in particular her twin, a Carmelite Sister, and her family, whom she calls her gang.

Sr Zoe O'Neill reflects that when I think of Pinner I think of a world in miniature peopled by Sisters, patients and staff who worked together, intermingling to bring new life and wholeness to broken bodies.

I was placed in Pinner in the early 1960s to commence my SRN training. In those days Pinner was linked to the Deaconesses' Hospital of the Prince of Wales in Tottenham.

We were able to do the first part of this combined training course in Pinner and then went on to complete the course at the Prince of Wales Hospital.

I received a good grounding in nursing working with Mrs Simes on the Women's Ward, then on the Babies' Ward with Sr Gerard, and of course in the classroom. On night duty we slept in the huts in the woods, with only the birds trilling us to sleep, and in winter we stepped over the snow that had seeped under the door!

After completing my SRN training, the Community asked me to train as a radiographer. As I did not have A level physics, I was put on night duty in the Private Block and spent my free time on a correspondence course in this subject; I'm glad to say I managed both somehow.

At night time I particularly remember Sr Kevin Thompson out with a torch light to frighten off the young nurses who were simply saying a loving good night to their boyfriends!

Pinner was and is a place, a home and a world where one unconsciously gives one's allegiance, one's loyalty forever. Like an extended family gathering, scattering, and come together again for meaningful occasions.

I had the great privilege of being part of that movement of St Vincent's going through different stages from being an orthopaedic hospital to its present nursing home status. Almost a full circle where some of us who gave care in the springtime of our years, now receiving support in the autumn of our lives.

Only those who have lived in Pinner know what being a 'Pinnerite' means. I am very proud and glad to be one of those.

THE CHAPEL

The Chapel rebuilt to replace the one bombed during the war was first used in January 1962 and was funded by the Sisters.

Rt Rev. Mgr M. Bidwell, Bishop of Miletopolis, was associated with St Vincent's for over 20 years, which was during the whole life of St Vincent's at the time. He held the position of Chairman of the Board of Management and requested to be buried at St Vincent's and so was laid to rest in the small consecrated ground in 1930, aged 58.

Many of the statues and furnishings within the new Chapel were donated. The Stations of the Cross and the altar come from the Daughters of Charity when the priory in Mill Hill closed.

They also transferred retired Sisters back to St Vincent's Nursing Home when it reopened in 2006. The two wooden carved statues in the Chapel were donations as is also the stained-glass crucifix, which is now the main altarpiece in the nursing home Chapel.

Left: Chapel and hospital site from the Sisters' House.

Below: The foundation stone for this Chapel was laid by Cardinal William Godfrey, 7th Archbishop of Westminster.

Bottom: The blessing of the foundation stone.

The Board of Management

request the pleasure of your company on the occasion of

The Blessing and Laying of the Foundation Stone of the re-built Chapel

at St. Vincent's Orthopaedic Hospital, Eastcote, Pinner, Middlesex

On Saturday, 8th July, 1961, at 3·30 p.m.

by

His Eminence Cardinal William Godfrey, D.D., Ph.D. Archbishop of Westminster

R.S.V.P. to: Sister Superior, St. Vincent's Orthopaedic Hospital, Eastcote, Pinner, Middlesex.

Tea will be served afterwards.

Inside the new
Chapel during
the 1960s to
1990s.

St Vincent's
Chapel: the
Stations of the
Cross were
hand-carved from
Oberammergau.

St Vincent's
Nursing Home
Chapel, with
the stained-glass
crucifix from the
original Chapel.

An appeal on ITV by John Barrie raised £3,662 and the plaque of St Vincent de Paul, sculpted by Charles Blakeman, was erected on the front of the Chapel.

The sculpture on the wall of the St Vincent's Nursing Home depicts the founder, St Vincent de Paul, sheltering children. With St Louise, he formed the Order of Sisters of Charity in Paris in 1633, to care for the sick and poor, and provide homes for abandoned children.

The Hospital Chapel replaces one bombed in 1941. Its Foundation Stone was laid in 1961 by Cardinal William Godfrey, 7th Archbishop of Westminster.

The relief of St. Vincent illustrated on the front cover is by Charles Blakeman.

The "lawn side" of the Chapel was once waste ground, and Bishop John Bidwell, a former member of the Board of Management, suggested it be tidied and lawned. The work completed, he casually remarked that he would like to be buried there.

In 1930 aged 58, he was the first to rest in the little cemetery. Also buried there are: Fr John Bebb, Chaplain from 1962 to 1969, who died in 1975 aged 58; Canon Denis Crowley, Chaplain from 1976 to 1980 when he died aged 69; and Elaine Redgrave, a patient of the Hospital who died in 1982 aged 15.

Anthony O'Connor, Doctor to the Sisters and Nurses for many years, was 69 when he died in 1982. His ashes and those of Harry Cobb, who was employed at the Hospital and died in 1986 are buried on the same land.

A crab apple tree and inscribed metal plate commemorate Anthony Janssens, Knight of St. Gregory, who died in 1984 aged 71. A Trustee and Chairman of the Board of Management, he was associated with the Hospital for 25 years.

Published by the Friends of St. Vincent's

Booklet produced by Fr Brown.

The image was used on the badge for nursing students who successfully completed their orthopaedic training at St Vincent's. The sculpture has pride of place on the wall of the nursing home.

The Rev. William Brown was resident Chaplain for many years and was well known for his many publications on prayer and the meaning of faith.

THE GRAIL

The Grail in Love Lane, Pinner, were always good friends with St Vincent's Hospital. They were a secular institute which had a close relationship with the Sisters, particularly during the time when children were a key feature of the hospital. The Grail had four elements: community, Grail companions, associate members and Grail partners. They largely provided education and took a key role in training people to share catechetic teaching and translation of Vatican documents. In the early days they gave talks to young Sisters on methods of teaching. The St Vincent's Sisters went every weekend to local churches.

The Sisters were allocated to various parishes within the area and included Sr Kevin to Ruislip, Sr Mary Joseph to Eastcote and Sr Genevieve to Northwood, who later became a Cistercian Sister, and has since returned to St Vincent's Nursing Home in her retirement. St Vincent's has maintained close links with the Grail in Pinner over many years. Strong friendships have been formed, and it was a great privilege for St Vincent's Nursing Home to have the opportunity of caring for Felicity Elwes from the Grail during the last years of her life.

SISTERS' HOUSE

A large building project commenced in 1964 and a year later the new Sisters' House was occupied, together with a new Chapel on the original site and a School of Nursing beside the physiotherapy department.

It was a great occasion for the Sisters. Previously the elderly Sisters lived in the original house while the 'young' Sisters lived in sheds at the end of the wards and in two sheds behind the theatre. No phones on wards, no lights, there had been no hot water, and often the ice was broken for morning tea! But it was all part of their dedication to poverty and light-hearted acceptance.

Christmas for the Sisters was also special and there would be presents around the decorated tree in the community room. Following midnight Mass they would gather with a 'glass of something', mince pies and wishes for a 'Happy Christmas'. The Chaplain once made a punch in a huge bowl and used a ladle to serve it to everyone. That year each Sister had an eiderdown for Christmas! Two big rooms in the house could be opened up for parties, celebrations and weekend nursing courses. Sr Angela Murray organised these for Sisters all over the country.

The Sisters stayed in the nurses' home and after various lectures would be taken to London in the hospital ambulance to see the lights. They invited visiting professors and experts to post-graduate training programmes.

When the Sisters' House was first built the Sisters always entered by the back door in order to preserve the stained-glass inner doors depicting St Catherine and St Vincent. The other windows in the hall were Community and Crest.

The first Superior had her office in the room on the right in the entrance.

AROUND EASTCOTE

The open nature of the district attracted several hospitals to the area. Mount Vernon Hospital, a branch of the North London Consumption Hospital founded in 1860, was built between 1902 and 1904 on a site south of the Rickmansworth Road, in the extreme north-west corner of the parish. Initially the hospital had 130 beds and was confined to the treatment of patients with tuberculosis. It was appointed a general hospital in 1929 and has since specialised in plastic surgery and cancer treatments. In 1962 the hospital had approximately 550 beds.

The Sisters' House, opened in 1964.

A cobalt unit for the treatment of deep-seated cancer – the first to be installed in this country – was given to the hospital by a Canadian organisation and has been operating since 1954.

The Northwood, Pinner and District Hospital in Pinner Road, Northwood, was originally housed in a small, hut-like building erected in 1919 as a war memorial. A more substantial building was erected in 1925 and extended in 1930.

The Roman Catholic parish of Ruislip was formed in 1921 with a temporary brick building housing a church and priest's house in Ruislip High Street and registered for worship. In 1933 the Roman Catholic population of Ruislip was said to number about 200 and in 1937 a Catholic primary school opened in Herlwyn Avenue. The old church in the High Street was replaced by the present Church of the Most Sacred Heart in Pembroke Road, built and consecrated in 1939.

The Roman Catholic parish of St Matthew's, covering the Northwood area, was founded in 1923. Services were held initially in a small building later used as a church hall. The present St Matthew's Church in Hallowell Road was opened in 1924.

The Church of St Thomas More in Field End Road, Eastcote, was opened in 1937, while the parish of St Thomas More, to which a priest was assigned, was formed in 1952.

For several years services were held in a scout hut in South Ruislip. In 1958 the parish of St Gregory the Great was created in the area south of the Yeading Brook in Victoria Road and consecrated in 1967. In 1962 services were being held in the St Swithun Wells and Bourne primary schools. The hospital as St Vincent's remains to serve the community in a different way.

During the 1960s children were still being admitted with childhood polio and paralysis, although the Salk vaccine was making an impression on this disease. Nevertheless, little had changed in general society by the 1960s but St Vincent's ensured opportunities were made available.

In 1963, 34 children ranging from the ages of four to 16 years were taken on a coach to Littlehampton. It was the fifth year this was organised and paid for by the Eastern Conference of the Society of St Vincent de Paul who ensured the girls in one coach and boys in the other arrived safely with a picnic, where their children from the Sacred Heart Ruislip Youth Club were waiting to give more help.

Judith Walker (*née* Hawkins) completed her nurse training at Charing Cross Hospital in 1963 and was soon to begin her training as a midwife. With a six-month gap she applied to Sr Angela for a nursing post at St Vincent's and worked mainly on the private block with Mrs Ferguson. There was a room she recalls at the far end of the ward that was set aside for the care of one or two elderly Sisters – it was nice to see them, comfortable in their old age and 'at home'.

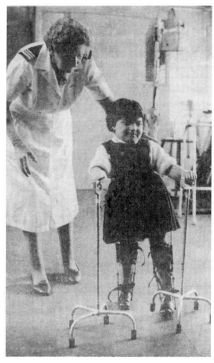

This little girl, Kathy Pearce, aged seven, is a patient at St. Vincent's Orthopaedic Hospital, at Northwood Hills. Here she is seen happily playing on the beach with her bucket and spade at Littlehampton, where she and 33 other children from the hospital were taken for their annual outing organised by the Society of St. Vincent de Paul. Story, more pictures, page 8.

Above left: Mick Illingworth, aged 10, using a frame to help him strengthen his arm muscles.

Above right: A young girl with polio is supported by a physiotherapist.

Left: A seaside trip to Littlehampton organised by the Society of St Vincent de Paul.

As her brother Philip had been a young polio patient in the 1950s on St Paul's Ward, she recalls meeting many of those boys for whom St Vincent's was home all those years ago. Following the completion of her midwifery training Judith married Ron Walker and settled in Ruislip.

During 1966 Judith returned to St Vincent's and spent many happy months on Holy Child Ward with Sisters Gabriel and Carmel, Mrs Honeyball and Mrs Edenbrough.

During this period, she cared for so many little girls and boys with tragic orthopaedic problems and cerebral palsy. Judith recalls twins Helen and Mary, and Wendy Henneker with fragilitis ossium, a challenging condition which causes spontaneous fractures. Wendy was a brave little girl, who was treated like a piece of fragile porcelain, always in pain but always smiling. Wendy remembers:

St Vincent's hosted gymkhanas and I was fascinated with the ponies.

The American air base at Northolt must have 'adopted' us for their charity because I remember at Christmas time they would come armed with presents. We were taken out to see the Royal Tournament Show, also the ice skating and the Bertram Mills Circus. I went to Lourdes five times, the last time being the centenary year in 1959.

Above: A seaside outing led by Eastcote Parish.

Right: Terry Eager on a trip to Gavarnie whilst on a pilgrimage to Lourdes.

A young lad called Terry Eager recalls his time at St Vincent's with fond memories and tells of his experience.

My first memory of St Vincent's was being brought down from Gateshead by ambulance and taken to Holy Child Ward. I was four years old and suffering with polio.

At about five years I moved to St Paul's Ward and this is where I had my first contact with Miss Kenna, who had a great influence on my life. She was a brilliant storyteller and if the boys had been good she would read a chapter from the 'Famous Five' by Enid Blyton. I loved the stories so I made sure the boys behaved.

On St Paul's there were over 26 boys, of these 21 were in some sort of frame, mostly to do with TB. I was called an 'up boy'. The polio had affected my left leg so I had to wear a calliper with a raised boot but that didn't stop me from doing things. I still got into fights, climbed trees and rode a bicycle. Schooling was a pleasure and each day I was happy to help set up the desks. Miss Roache was in charge and she travelled from London every day on the train.

Sr Kevin came in on a Tuesday; even today I can reel off facts of general knowledge learned from the women.

On the ward we used the big green roller screens and pretended we were having plays. I can remember snow coming into the ends of the beds. Every day we were given a spoon of malt, all the boys all with one spoon!

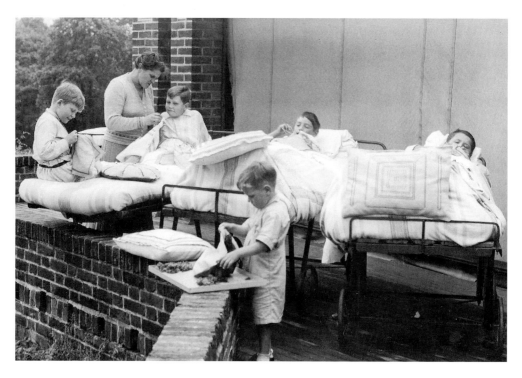

Miss Roache and the boys are busy making cushions.

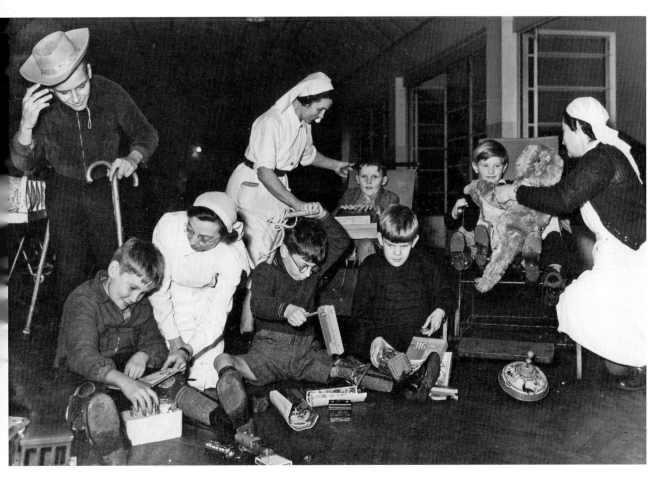

St Paul's Ward: Miss Kenna and Miss Byrne.

My most treasured memory was when the Royal Canadian Mounted Police came to visit us in the Coronation year. The men seemed like giants, one of them placed a hat on my head.

The children who didn't have visitors had their clothes made in the work room run by Sr Agnes and Miss Mahon. We were all dressed the same. Up to the age of about 11 I thought I was an orphan. It was only when my eldest sister tracked me down that I realised I came from a large family.

I used to serve at Mass most days. I was taught to walk, kneel and sit correctly during Mass and with due reverence. We were taught that being an altar server was a privilege.

I remember Benediction was much loved and well attended. First a litany (often of divine praises), followed by *O Salutaris*, *Tantum Ergo* and the Benediction. The incense provided the odour of sanctity, and a final rousing hymn rounded off the ceremony.

A great sadness was that a lot of my friends died of their illnesses so I was well used to serving at their funerals.

Far left: Canadian Mounties visiting St Vincent's, 1950s.

Left: Terry Eager on First Communion day.

I met Wilfred Pickles and his wife Mabel in 1964 when he hosted a 'live' Christmas special from the hospital for their annual Home Service Christmas Day Broadcast. Wilfred Pickles was a radio celebrity who also pursued an acting career in West End theatre. He was awarded the OBE for services to broadcasting in 1950.

His most significant work was as host of the BBC Radio show *Have A Go*, which ran from 1946 to 1967. This was one of the most popular shows ever broadcast; at its peak in the 1950s it attracted an audience of over 20 million. Wilfred and his wife Mabel took the programme to church halls all over the country, 'bringing the people to the people'.

Pickles interviewed ordinary people who were encouraged to tell heart-warming stories and share their experiences, and who were invited to answer quiz questions for money prizes.

I think my unhappiest memories at St Vincent's were when I moved up to St Michael's Ward at the age of 11. This came as a big shock to me, I suppose I then had to grow up. My feelings were mixed because to me I belonged at St Vincent's, yet I had a large family up North.

I left the hospital when I was 14 to go and live with my dad, but he was a complete stranger. My stepmother was awful to me, and I asked to go back 'home' to the hospital at 15. I started as an apprentice shoe maker. I was given a room in the men's home.

This is when I got to know Sr Joseph, she was good to all her lads and she became a trusted friend. Sr Joseph allowed me to use her camera, she let me develop the photography in the X-ray's dark room and I retain an interest in photography.

I can remember Sr Joseph organising Passion plays with the staff and nurses when I was a centurion.

I met my wife Annette when she used to come with her father to help at events organised by the Naval Reserves at Northwood.

I lived and worked at the hospital until I married and moved to Northampton in 1972. The Sisters did a grand job looking after me, they also came to the church on my wedding day.

I still keep in touch with Sr Joseph who is now known as Sr Mary Jo, also with Gerry Smith who worked in the splint room. I kept in touch with Miss Kenna up until she died – she was like a mother to me.

I was part of a large 'family' at St Vincent's, since then I have got back in touch with my natural family. I am very proud to have a good wife, three daughters, six grandsons and one great-granddaughter.

I am still making handmade shoes and as part of the Cultural Olympiad a giant 'Godiva' was made in Coventry, while Northampton's offering was a pair of handmade boots 'size 72'.

Above left: Terry and wife Annette with their daughters, Teresa, Yvonne and Diane. (Photo permission by Terry Eager.)

Above right: Terry Eager's grandchildren. (Photo permission by Terry Eager.)

Left: Terry lasting the boot. (Photo permission by Terry Eager.)

Left: Terry and colleagues at Horace Batten Boot Makers of Ravensthorpe – seven generations of boot-making (photo permission by Terry Eager).

Right: Some boys with Rev. John Galvin, who transferred to St Patrick's, Soho, in 1968.

> My part in this venture was the lasting of the boots, welting the soles and finishing the boots.
>
> 'Godiva' made her way down to London to Westminster Hall, and on the way she called by several towns, collecting gifts.
>
> The boots are now kept at Northampton's Boot and Shoe Museum.

The workshops were now producing a gross annual income in the region of £6,000.

In 1965 the Variety Club of Great Britain presented a minibus to the hospital in a scheme sponsored by Fred Pontin – famous for Pontin's Holidays. It could carry 14 seated children or six wheelchairs and this welcome gift allowed house-bound children to enjoy outings which would otherwise be impossible.

The local school children were very involved with the youngsters on the wards. St Nicholas Grammar School for boys and St Mary's School for girls, which have since merged to become Haydon School in Northwood Hills, spent many happy hours playing games. Ian Bayliss recalls playing board games as a 14-year-old such as chess, ludo and draughts with the 'bed boys' and Keith Bayliss would often help with the washing up.

In 1966 the decrease in length of stay was a significant marker in the development of orthopaedics. The earliest figures available are for 1933 and indicate that the average length of stay in the hospital was 424.5 days – by the early 1980s it had reduced to 24 days and in the mid-1990s in some hospitals you could have a major hip replacement and be home in five days.

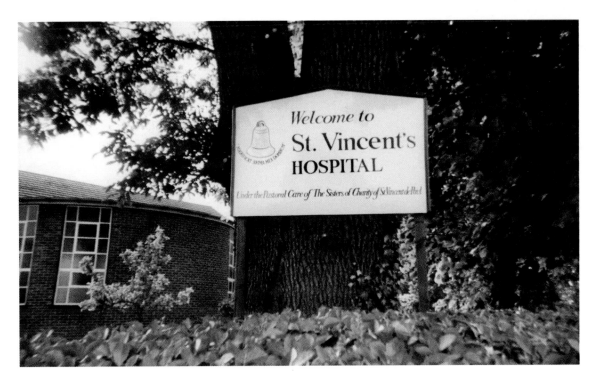

Main entrance, 1999.

ST. VINCENT'S ORTHOPAEDIC HOSPITAL

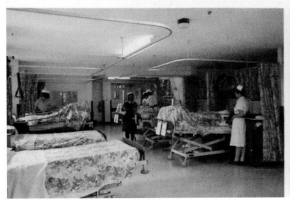

Postcard of the hospital.

THE "A.L." OFFICIAL SERIES.

LOG-BOOK

OF THE

St Vincent's R.C Home for Physically Defective Children, Eastcote.   No. 29547.

SCHOOL.

Middlesex. Local Education Authority.

To be kept by the Principal Teacher.

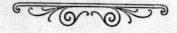

E. J. ARNOLD & SON, LTD., EDUCATIONAL PUBLISHERS, LEEDS AND GLASGOW.

Above left: Scouts badge with crutches.

Above right: The 4th Northwood Middlesex Scouts in the 'Dell' at St Vincent's.

Left: Front page of the School Register: St Vincent's R.C. Home for Physically Defective Children, Eastcote, No: 29547.

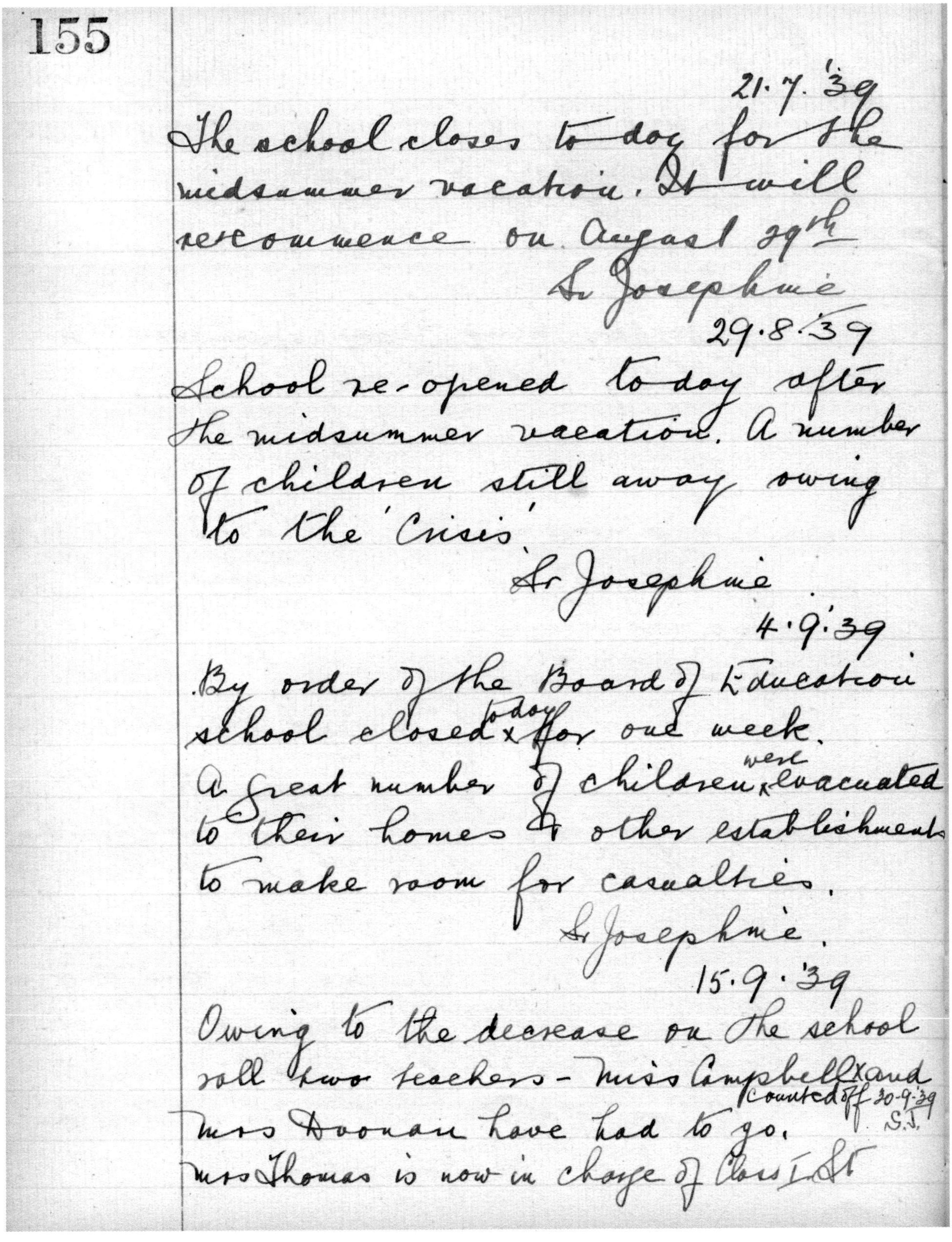

21.7.'39

The school closes to-day for the midsummer vacation. It ~~will~~ recommence on August 29th

Sr Josephine

29.8.'39

School re-opened to-day after the midsummer vacation. A number of children still away owing to the 'Crisis'.

Sr Josephine.

4.9.'39

By order of the Board of Education school closed ~~x~~ for one week. to-day
A great number of children were evacuated to their homes & other establishments to make room for casualties.

Sr Josephine.

15.9.'39

Owing to the decrease on the school roll ~~two~~ teachers — Miss Campbell ~~x~~ and Mrs Doonan have had to go. Counted off 30-9-39 S.J.
Mrs Thomas is now in charge of Class I &

School Register indicating the evacuation of some of the children to other establishments to make room for casualties.

replaced by Miss O'Shea who commenced duties to-day on St. Margaret's Ward. Miss Hickey resumed duties to-day after her illness.

Sr Josephine.

30·1·'45

Owing to the severity of the weather a half-holiday has been granted. For the past three weeks it has been impossible for written or handwork of any kind. Oral work, spelling bees, tables reading, wireless, singing and games have replaced these exercises.

Sr Josephine

15·2·45.

H.M.I Dr. Bywaters inspected school to-day and examined all classes in school and workshops.

Sister Josephine

School Register, 1945: adapting the syllabus.

21st September 1952

Gerry Smith started to train in tailor's shop attending afternoons only. Kathleen Blackaller started domestic training to day attending mornings only.

Sr. Kevin

24th September 1952

Miss Roche absent this afternoon to see specialist, her class was taken by

Sister Kevin

23rd & 24th October 1952

School closed for mid-term holidays

Sr. Kevin

27th October school re-opened All members of staff in attendance.

Sr Kevin

25th November 1952

Miss Hickey absent to-day on account of illness

Sr. Kevin

Excerpt from the School Register, 1952: Gerry Smith starts his training in the tailors' workshop.

Above: The current chapel altar.

Right: St Vincent's stained glass, depicting two babies and a child.

Below: The St Vincent's Gymkhana silver cups.

Above left: Staff who worked in St Vincent's. Left to right: Stephen Lovell, Jan, Debbie McCarroll and Cynthia Kamara, Ward Sister.

Above right: Staff working in the wards. Left to right: Juliette Hurran, Sr Stella, Debbie McCarroll, Stuart and Teresa Kelly.

Left: Bob Holness opens the Annual Garden Fete in 1998.

Above: A stained–glass window in the Sisters' House.

Left: Sr Zoe O'Neil DC.

Below: Back row, left to right: Sr Mgt Brady DC, Sr Mai O'Connor DC, Sr Maria Robb DC. Seated: Sr Carmel Cussen DC, Sr Aine McGuinness DC, Sr Clare O'Driscoll DC.

Far left: Children helping each other.

Left: Terry is on the left; John Denning and Aiden Barry wait with rose petals for the procession for Our Lady.

Above left: Happy little boy living at St Vincent's.

Above right: The administrative team.

Left: Rev. William Brown following a baptism, with Senior Nurse Laraya's family.

Above: Front drive.

Left: St Vincent de Paul.

Below: New Chapel, 1961.

Above left: Daughters of Charity, 1964.

Above right: Sr Gerard Wood, Pinner.

Below: Miss Kenna at home.

The front cover of *Nursing Times* with Sr Cynthia Kamara, Orthopaedic Ward Sister, and one of her patients.

Staff Nurse Jenny Yexley and Sr Maureen Eaton.

Above: Fr Bebb and the student nurses in the 1970s.

Below: Violetta Laraya, Mariesa Kirwin, Sr Carmel, Sr Clare and Irene Heywood Jones.

Sr Clare DC
teaches students
on the lower
floor of the
nursing school,
which is used as
a demonstration
and practical
room.

Sr Christine
Wholley DC,
outpatients
department.

Back class – one
of many held for
inpatients and
outpatients.

Left: League of Friends: Vic Middlemiss, Nick Cutcliffe and Kathleen Noakes.

Below left: League of Friends: John Young and Peter Cloot.

Below right: John Young (far left), Chairman of the League of Friends, 1999.

Bottom: Maryanne Matthews, Staff Nurse, Rose Barr, Night Sister, Mr Barr, and Vic Middlemiss, League of Friends secretary.

Above: Garden Fete, 1998 – the grand raffle draw.

Below: Sr Jane Doran DC at the Annual Garden Fete, 1998.

Above: Bob Holness declaring the Garden Fete open, 1998.

Below: Fete day, 1998: children of one of the staff members look at some photos of the children in the 'Old St Vincent's'.

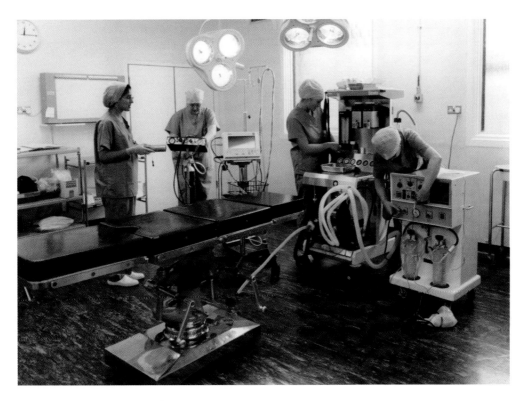

Above: Modern operating theatre.

Below: X-ray department, 1980s.

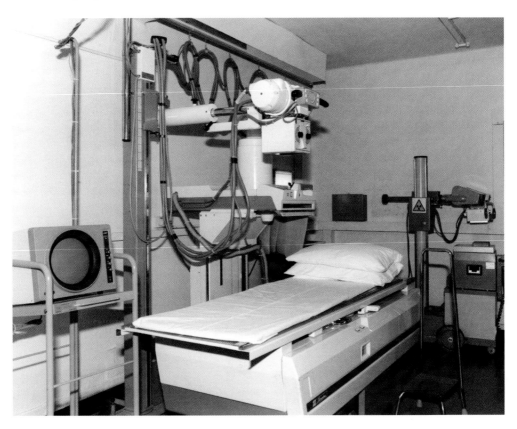

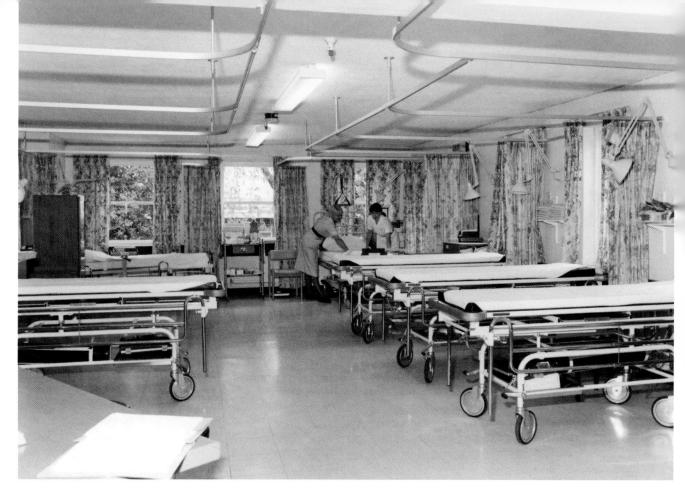

Post–operative recovery ward, 1970–1990s.

Orthopaedic ward, 1970–1990s.

Above: Alan Edmondson, Trustee.

Left: Sr Carmel DC and Captain Donald Woodhouse OBE. Captain Don was a regular visitor to St Vincent's and was commissioned as a Church Army evangelist and served as a lay minister for almost 70 years.

Below: Sr Angela, Sr Mary Jo and Sr Carmel.

Hospital staff watching the eclipse: Kevin Sharratt; Wendy; Diane Holmes; Sr Christine; Sr Carmel, HR adviser; Judi Corti; Moira Newman; Jacquie Scott, receptionist and Jeannette Dunbar.

Shop volunteers. Left to right: Sr Mary Jo Powell DC, Sr Christine Wholley DC, Margaret Bayliss and Joyce White.

Above left: Jacquie Scott, CEO/Director of Nursing, and Peter Cloot, League of Friends Chairman in 1998 following the Adjournment Debate in the House of Commons led by John Wilkinson, MP for Hillingdon.

Above right: Sisters' House, 1990s. Left to right: Sr Paula Kearon, Sr Carmel Cussen, Sr Christine Wholley, Sr Angela Murray, Sr Joseph Byrne and Sr Marion Daly.

Left to right: Sr Patricia Sylke DC, Sr Angela Murray DC and Sr Jane Doran DC.

A fire engulfs St Vincent's.

Left: The London Fire Brigade in full action and Jacquie speaking to the Chairman.

Below: What was left: burned-out embers.

Above: The foundations are laid.

Left: Trustees from left to right: Jacquie Scott, Alan Edmondson and John Davern, early 2006.

Below: The original Holm Oak was salvaged.

Opposite page, above left: The Unclear Path: Life Beyond Disability by Liz Greeley.

Opposite page, above right: Royal Air Force cadets, 1998.

Opposite page, below: St Vincent's Prayer Group inspect the building progress, 2004. Back, far left: Joan Worland and her husband Edward (not clearly visible). Foreground, left to right: Nick Foley, Clare Craigie Williams, Pauline Neighbour; far right: Maureen O'Donavan, Isabel Rodgers and Sr Carmel Cussen DC. Far left: Jacquie Scott.

Left: Board of Trustees, 2006. Left to right: Raymond Davern, Philip Jukes, Geralyn Wynne, John Davern, Jacquie Scott, Alan Edmondson and Dr Margaret Price.

Below: Priests from all the local parishes who concelebrated the Holy Mass with His Eminence Cardinal Cormack Murphy O'Connor, including: John Davern, Chairman; Alan Edmondson, Trustee; Jacquie Scott, Trustee; Rev. Ray Armstrong, resident Chaplain; and Rev. Bob Barry, resident.

Above left: Jacquie Scott, Trustee, and John Davern, Chair of St Vincent's Nursing Home.

Above right: A registered nurse meets the cardinal.

Left: John Davern, Chairman; Rev. Michael O'Connor, St Thomas More parish priest; His Eminence Archbishop Cormac Murphy O'Connor; and Jacquie Scott, Trustee, 2006.

Official opening of St Vincent's, 2006.

Back row, standing, left to right: David Blythe, Colin Furness, Sr Christine Wholley DC, Ann Reid, Sr Carmel Cussen DC, Anne McDonald, Jacquie Scott, Beryl Giradot, Shelia Griffith, David Roland, Ray Plummer, John Davern. Seated, left to right: Petal Connell, Alan Edmondson, Juliette Hurren.

Right: Mrs Margaret Davern, Cathy O'Sullivan, Jacquie Scott, Trustee, and Shiria Halsey, Matron.

Below: Kathleen O'Sullivan and Sr Anne de Sousberghe, here 109 years old, at Holy Souls Community.

Ray, David and Colin at the annual garden party.

Above left: Michael McKane, Ray and Cheryl Plummer at the garden party.

Above right: Raised beds are in place for the 'gardening club'.

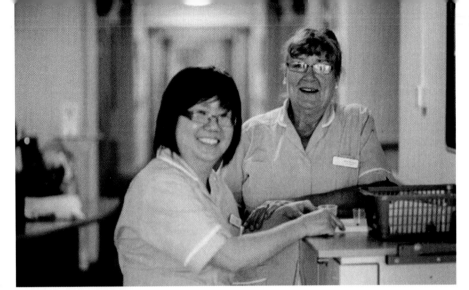

Working at St Vincent's.

Preparing dinner.

St Vincent's receptionists, Sue and Lyn.

Above left: CEO/Director of Nursing, Jacquie Scott.

Above centre: Colin Furness, accounts team.

Above right: Shiria Halsey, Matron, 2006.

Far left: Sr Josephine O'Mahoney DC and Sr Aine McGuiness DC.

Left: Summer birthday party, 2005.

Margaret Edmondson and Alan Edmondson with Sr Carmel Cussen DC.

Opposite page, above: Main reception.

Opposite page, below: St Vincent's Nursing Home, 2006.

St Vincent's Centenary Ball at Moor Park Mansion, 2012.

Conversely, the number of surgical procedures has shown a steady increase and the number of beds in use almost halved.

The number of beds decreased to 141, while the weekly cost per patient increased to £30 10s 8d. and simultaneously an entirely new provision of care was introduced, with the opening of St Mary's Ward for children with cerebral palsy educational sub-normality. It accommodated 10 boys and 10 girls, and was largely funded by the Spastics Society.

In 1974 a mouth-operated typewriter was presented to St Mary's Ward, enabling patients to resume written contact with their friends and relatives, made difficult by arthritis or paralysis.

Ordinary school methods were unsuitable to meet these children's needs, and the hospital was very grateful for the gift of specialised teaching aids to facilitate learning.

The picture opposite shows the nurses' home during the 1960s. The paved area bordered by the low wall is the area where the conservatory once sat. More modernisation and alterations took place inside the nurses' home during 1969, and an anonymous donation provided a new set of beds.

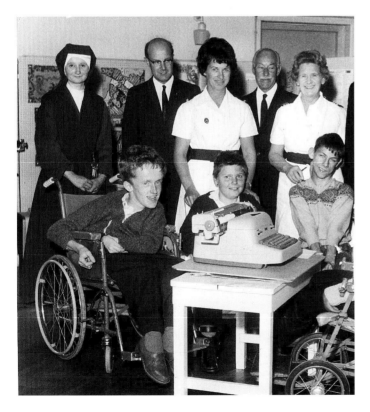 

Above left: Sr Anne Remmen DC and the Hoover Company managers, who have donated a typewriter.

Above right: Left to right: Chairman Tony Janssens, Cardinal Heenan and Sr Genevieve (Matron), opening St Mary's Ward, 1967.

Above: Bishop Mahon, Sr Genevieve, Sr Joseph and the health visitors.

Below: The nurses' sitting room, which until 1910 had been the drawing room.

Left: Main entrance, 1970s.

Below: Nurses came from all over the world to St Vincent's, 1970.

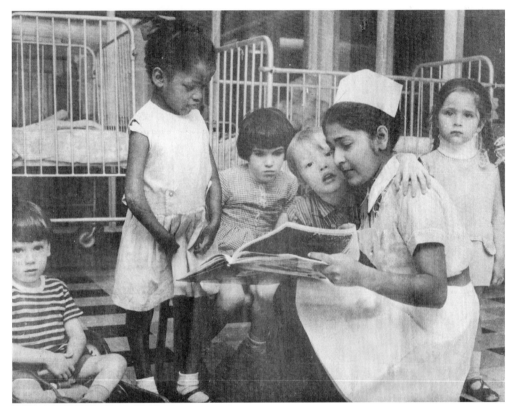

The main house had altered little but the administration offices were renovated in 1978.

Captain Formby KSG resigned as Chairman of the Board of Management in 1969 but remained a Trustee until his death in 1977. Anthony Janssens succeeded him as Chairman.

– HEADLONG INTO THE 1970S –

Sister Genevieve Bergin DC was Matron from 1972 to 1974. Ruislip Clinic was at the time the only clinic left which, during 40 years of attendances, had doubled and it supplied physiotherapy to adults. The weekly cost per inpatient continued to rise and was now £48.37 for decimalisation had overtaken the imperial system.

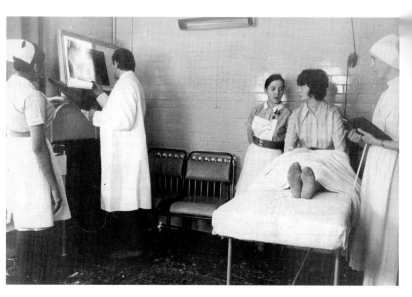

Above left: Miss Eileen Peterson, in charge of the physiotherapy team in the Ruislip Clinic, retires after 34 years, here joined by Fr John Galvin and Sr Angela Murray.

Above right: Mr Crawford Adams, Sr Margaret and the team reviewing X-rays.

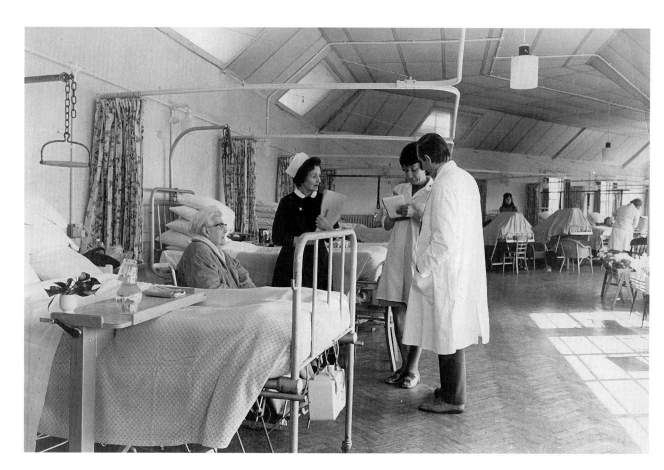

Ward round with Sr Simes.

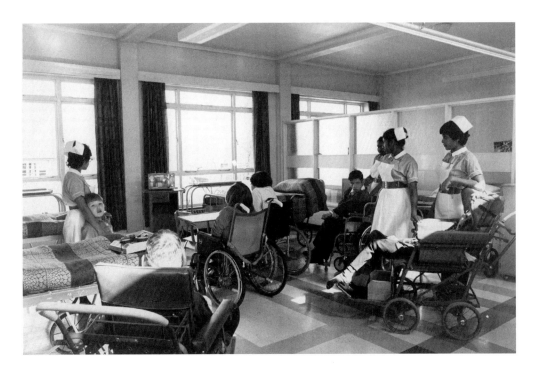

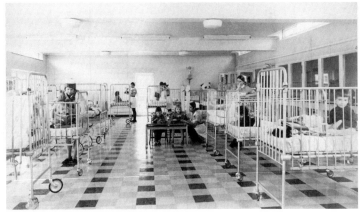

Above: The Children's Ward.

Left: Holy Child Ward.

Father Bebb was a very gregarious, outgoing and ecumenically minded priest. He established the parish council, built the parish centre and set up a comprehensive catechetical programme for the younger parishioners. He also played a significant role in 'Churches Together' in Northwood, eventually being elected as Chairman.

Father Bebb became parish priest at St Matthew's Church in Northwood and a room in the parish centre is named after him. Father Bebb had been a prisoner of war of the Japanese and it was probably those hardships he suffered which contributed to his early death with a heart attack at the age of 59.

He told us he had been engaged to be married at the time of his capture. While a prisoner he received what he described as a 'divine kick up the pants' and decided to try his vocation for the priesthood when he was released.

St Vincent's main
entrance in the
1970s and 80s.

He wondered how he would break the news to his fiancée, only to discover that he had been reported 'believed killed in action' and she had married someone else!

On one occasion 11 o'clock Mass at St Vincent's was televised by ITV, celebrated by the hospital Chaplain Fr John Bebb. The choir was provided by St Luke's Church, Pinner, and the altar servers were all former patients of the hospital.

Fr Bebb combined his St Vincent's role with being adviser to the ITV on Roman Catholic affairs and had broadcast several important occasions on behalf of the Church, including the ceremonial crowning of Pope Paul in St Peter's Square and the enthronement of Cardinal Heenan at Westminster Cathedral.

Perhaps a small proportion of his vast audience were aware that he was resident Chaplain of St Vincent's Orthopaedic Hospital.

The Diamond Jubilee of the hospital at Eastcote in May 1972 was celebrated by Cardinal Heenan at a Mass in the Chapel, after which he formally opened the School of Nursing.

By 1973 the Variety Club minicoach was well worn out. The Harrow branch of the Rotary Club provided a new one, greatly improved by the addition of an electrically operated tail-lift, allowing access for wheelchairs without pushing them up a ramp.

David the driver worked at St Vincent's for nearly 20 years and drove everything from hospital vehicles and ambulances to the electric vehicle, attending various functions from taking people around the hospital from ward to department to collecting blood from Mount Vernon for people who were having surgery, or taking patients on 'home visits' with the therapy staff to see if they could manage at home after surgery.

The operating theatre was improved in 1973 and then had major alterations in the late 1980s as the number of operations performed had risen to about 1,000 each year.

Above left: Children's outing with David, the hospital driver for 20 years.

Above: Meeting the animals.

Left: Sisters at the seaside.

Below: Windsor Castle day trip.

The X-ray department was also improved in 1973 with a new machine, and during 1980 there were 4,810 X-ray examinations. During the same year, the outpatients' department provided 29,653 treatments. Radiologist Dr Brailsford visited weekly to report on X-rays.

There were few children at the hospital by the 1970s.

As a result, in 1974, St Mary's Ward was converted to care for chronically ill adults long-term. Sixteen patients suffering from such conditions as multiple sclerosis and Huntingdon's chorea were transferred at the request of the Regional Health Authority from a women's nursing home in Maidenhead which was closing down. Patients were transported by the new mini-coach.

 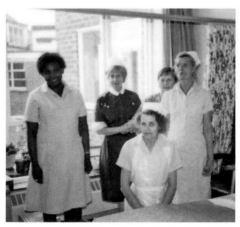

Above left: New mini-coach. Left to right: Tom McManamon, Chairman of the Garden Fete Committee; Sister Snider; Colin Carne, Hospital Secretary; Sr Carmel DC; and Vivian Stenham in the wheelchair.

Above right: Sr Sherry, Ward Sister of St Mary's Ward.

Above left: Dorothy O'Mahoney and Joan Handford in 1981 with the comforts trolley on St Mary's Ward.

Above right: Hospital amenities shop, 1970s.

Juliette Hurran, occupational therapy assistant.

Sr Elizabeth Armstrong DC was Matron from 1973 to 1977 and ensured that St Vincent's Hospital maintained its usual momentum. She was a vibrant and energetic woman who moved on to be a hospital Chaplain at the Royal London Hospital, dying after a long and illustrious career in 2012.

Cynthia Kamara, a nurse originally from Sierra Leone, recalls her introduction to the St Vincent's way:

> I first heard of St Vincent's Hospital in 1982 while I was working at the local general district hospital in Northwood.
>
> I was accepted for the orthopaedic nurse training programme in 1983. In 1984-1999 I was employed on the staff, latterly as the Sister on the ward for long-term adult care.
>
> The hospital's grounds were beautiful, surrounded by a natural ancient woodland, one of the rare places in the London suburb of Northwood Hills. This is where you can still find not only foxes, squirrels and even snakes, but also rare birds and the most adorable deer like Bambi.
>
> Every clinical was single storey so it was easy for patients to see these animals, which could easily stray into the wards if not guarded!
>
> When I first saw a fox sitting proudly on the balcony of St Teresa's Ward, my reaction was, 'Oh, here is a wolf!' to which Janet, the physiotherapist, laughed endearingly.

The environment was aimed at the rapid rehabilitation and discharge of patients. Discharge plans were easily tailored to the length of stay – those having long-term care in St Mary's Ward we transferred to nursing and residential homes. We had a great time caring for patients and it never felt like a hospital.

I also have fond memories of the activities during the summer, mainly the summer fete, on one occasion opened by the late Bob Holness (the television presenter of *Blockbusters*).

We had some great characters amongst the staff, with a large Irish community. The nuns were humane and pleasant to work with, teaching by example a lot about dignity and respect for others.

The hospital closed in 1999 as a result of reorganisation of the NHS, which was our main commissioner, and I have subsequently worked at Northwick Park Hospital, Harrow.

There are many characters who have lived their lives within the boundaries of St Vincent's, notably Harry Cobb, who worked in the kitchen. His wife Joan often visits his grave.

Teresa Kelly worked as an auxiliary nurse on St Mary's Ward and is the cousin of Laurence Christopher Carey, son of Mr Carey, who was in charge of the gardens. Bridget Mary Carey, who also used to work on the domestic staff at St Vincent's Hospital, is Laurence's wife. The Carey family – like many others – have a long association with St Vincent's.

Teresa Kelly, Sr Stella and a patient on St Mary's Ward.

Above left: The staff from the hospital enjoy time together. Left to right: Debbie McCarroll, nursing auxiliary; Sr Pauline Forde DC, Ward Sister on St Vincent's Ward; Mrs Maggie Gibbs, HR; Caroline Blom, RGN; Sheila Swain, RGN.

Above right: Nursing auxiliary Peggy Warby worked on St Mary's Ward.

PETAL CONNELL, 1975

I moved to Ruislip in April 1975 and started working at St Vincent's as night sister in November when Sr Elizabeth was the Matron. Having specialised in orthopaedic care prior to having my children, I felt fortunate to find a hospital for orthopaedics with a good reputation in the community and high standards of care.

On St Marys Ward we cared for 22 young chronic sick patients; some had suffered strokes, others suffered progressive neurological disorders such as multiple sclerosis, motor neurone disease or Huntingdon's chorea.

We were able to boast that bedsores were a rare occurrence due to good nursing practice. Some patients had difficulty adjusting when eager visitors were loath to leave and occasionally (although I was not a Catholic at the time) I found that a quiet prayer, such as Hail Mary or Our Father, which had been such a great part of one lady's life brought peace of mind.

Initially I worked on alternate nights while my daughter was young, eventually increasing to three consecutive nights. The nights following the days when Mr Braddock and Mr Philips operated were busy and the team worked well to maintain the care which you would wish for your own family. I felt pleased after I left in the mornings that we had done a good job.

The staff turnover was very low and the atmosphere and nursing care standards remained very good. There was no time or space for complacency, although this was not to say that there were not some funny or strange things occurring!

The hospital was located on both sides of the road which led to the woods and as there were no lights, each night sister carried a torch.

One night a group of four young men were around the premises and I asked them to leave. I was told they were visiting a patient and were not prepared to go. I said I would call the ward but they did not seem deterred and so I also threatened to call the police and wondered at this point what they might do to stop me. There was some verbal jostling but they did not seem too bothered and between them there was some anxiety developing and they were beginning to worry about my threat until one of the boys replied, 'What her, the old bag?' I had never been so glad to be an 'old bag'!

In later years security lights were erected and, crossing the car park, I saw the shadows following me closely…I froze, held on tight to the bunch of keys strategically poised in my hand and announced, 'I know you are there' and turned round … to find it was my own shadow. I laughed out loud! Had anyone come up the hill then they would have thought, 'poor soul, she should be put away'.

I worked in the hospital for 24 years, in which time many protocols, demands and policies changed. One thing remained the same, the caring and compassion and that everyone was treated with respect. I can only say I was grateful to have been able to do a job well and to have worked with others who shared my philosophy and ethos in life.

The splint workshop closed in 1974. Inflation pushed the weekly cost per patient up to a staggering £157.72 although the boot workshop contributed £12,456 to the income that year.

St Vincent's was very busy in 1977. The patient numbers rose, admitting 939 into 113 beds and surgical intervention for 752 people was managed without a major impact on the running costs.

Night Sister Petal Connell and Chairman Ben Turner.

A joint venture with Hillingdon Area Health Authority and Social Services under a contractual arrangement met the cost of the NHS beds. St Vincent's had set aside 10 private rooms/beds to boost the income.

The number of children in the hospital diminished because developments in preventative medicine and obstetric care, together with changes in orthopaedic treatment meant that conditions could be diagnosed early and children treated as outpatients.

Beverley Ellie recalls her experience as a young girl on the children's ward:

From what I have been told, I was admitted to the Holy Child Ward when a baby of three months.

This was my first home, where I felt that I belonged. I underwent many operations and procedures there and into my teens I was returning for surgery. I did not like the pre-medication they gave me as they made me feel sick and I still have a healthy fear of needles. I was always worried I would not go back to Holy Child after the surgery. There was discipline with the right quantity of love.

Looking back now, I look at those times as really being the best part of my growing up. The Sisters were amazing and contributed to the person I am today. I am now a mother, a role I love very much. We are both in contact with a few of the Sisters who had worked in Holy Child Ward.

Visitors were an important part of life at St Vincent's and I recall the first time I met Elaine, who was to become a firm friend. I was about five and she was three. We loved to play together and I remember one day we chased a beautiful butterfly all around the ward.

We led a very sheltered life but very secure and loving; as far as we were concerned potatoes came mashed, fish in fingers and bread was white, sliced and buttered! We were well fed and nurtured and Carmella who did the cooking and housekeeping kept us in order. We felt very important when we were allowed to go out around the grounds to play.

Valerie Redgrave recalls that as a young girl she used to visit St Vincent's with her mother and she found this an emotional experience. It was many years later that, as a young woman in the Royal Naval Reserve in Northwood, she joined in a visit to St Vincent's to assist in organising a Christmas party for the children and young people who lived at the hospital.

Not many of the children on Holy Child Ward were able to attend, but one young girl with a wide smile was Beverley and her friend Elaine.

My husband Malcolm and I were captivated by these young children and it was not too long before we were visiting them regularly at weekends. The children in the ward all slept in high-sided cots but those who were able were encouraged to be out and playing and it was a frequent sight to see a Sister, white robes flapping, chasing after one of the small children, all smiles and laughter.

Beverley and Elaine were soon coming on outings with us both to the parks, visiting relatives, going shopping and generally enjoying life. I remember the day that on one of our many day trips Beverley went for her first train journey from Eastcote Station. She had never seen a real train before and she saw this large object looming towards her from a distance as the train approached the platform as though a monster was coming towards her and for a short while she was quite hysterical on the platform.

Life at St Vincent's was, to modern eyes, very restricted but the stability and love offered there stood Beverley and Elaine in good stead in the difficult days to come. We had been married just over a year and were not Catholic (Elaine was), we were not mixed race and we had no experience of bringing up children. All obstacles which these days would probably have prevented Elaine from becoming our child. With a recommendation from the Sisters at St Vincent's Elaine was officially adopted by us in March 1972. Very soon after this it became apparent that Elaine was not well.

Valerie recalls that,

Beverley had a family but they did not visit and did not want her adopted, and initially social workers advised us to stop all contact with her – we felt this would have been unkind and so we continued to visit and have her to stay with us.

Beverley and Elaine continued to be a part of our family and were delighted when two more daughters were added to the family. While Beverley was under the care of Westminster Social Services, after she left St Vincent's, we became her social 'aunt and uncle'.

Elaine's health continued to decline and after 10 years of illness she died in her father's arms. She is buried at St Vincent's surrounded by her family and

Beverley and her son Alex,
now at university.

friends. St Vincent's and the Sisters changed the life of our family – through them we gained a wonderful daughter who was a delight to all who knew her and we have Beverley as an addition to our family with her lovely son.

Beverley was a long-term patient with Sr Pauline Forde DC on the children's ward. Sr Pauline still keeps in touch with 'Bev', who refers to her as mother!

Debbie McCarroll, now on the staff of St Vincent's Nursing Home first met Sr Pauline at the age of 11. Debbie had treatment for her hip; she kept in touch with Sr Pauline and fellow patients and refers to Sr Pauline as a 'life-long friend' who attended her wedding – a family friend.

Sr Pauline also worked on the male ward St Vincent's and kept a very well organised and efficient ward where the students learned a great deal and the patients wanted for nothing and received high-quality nursing care.

A colleague reflects on their memories of the fete day when Sr Pauline, 'the backroom girl', ran the hospital while 'we ran the stalls and showed VIPs around. What a relief to know that all was well behind the scenes.'

Another staff member recalls a male patient with fractures after a bad road accident. On discharge he met a priest who remarked afterwards, 'this man was healed physically, mentally and spiritually, I am so glad that you practise the "holistic" method.' This word had arrived!

Sr Pauline followed up old patients and staff in need – the assistant gardener retired to Northwood Blind Home (war injury), the old cleaner in Coleshill Nursing Home and many others keep in touch with her.

Sr Pauline now works as a parish Sister and Chaplain to a London hospital and lives in Pinner.

Holy Child Ward was closed but was refurbished as Holy Child House, a much-needed resource for 12 multi-handicapped children. It was supported by the London Borough of Hillingdon, Hillingdon Area Health Authority and St Vincent's Board of Management to provide care, rehabilitation and education.

The beds were funded by the Ruislip Branch of the Round Table, and much of the equipment was given by the Rotary Club of Pinner/Northwood, local public houses and organisations. Holy Child House was officially opened in 1978 by Reverend Gerald Mahon, Bishop of West London.

Petal Connell a senior night sister who worked at St Vincent's for 24 years, recalls the care provided for children:

Holy Child provided short-term care for babies and small children with a wide variety of physical and neurological problems, giving respite care to parents and families. Holy Child was small and gave great support and care to the children who could present so many difficulties which had to be interpreted with incredible care and attention.

Above left: Bishop Gerald Mahon, Bishop of West London.

Above right: The sandpit provided by the Lions Club.

Below: St Vincent's Ward in the 1980s, with views across Harrow towards Crystal Palace. Note the change of the nurses' uniform.

Above left: Some members of St Vincent's Board, including Bishop Craven, Fr O'Daly and Miss Bacon.

Above right: Mr and Mrs Anthony Janssens, Cardinal Basil Hume and Sr Carmel Cussen DC.

The interaction between the parents, child and nursing staff required trust and understanding on the highest level. Great 'in-depth' discussions ensued during some nights.

In fine weather the veranda was used as an extension of the play area. Children aged five to 16 could be accepted on a long- or short-term basis or as a respite facility to help families.

In 1978 the Ruislip Lions provided a play area for the children. It covered the site of the old schoolroom.

The Matron appointed to the role in 1978 managing all clinical activity was Sr Carmel Cussen DC RGN ONC.

The key members of the Board of Management at the time included His Eminence Cardinal George Basil Hume, Archbishop of Westminster, Chairman Anthony Janssens and Ben Turner, Vice Chairman. Lead clinicians at the time were Dr J. Rubie, paediatrician, Mr Harrold, Mr Howse, Mr Phillips, Mr Braddock, Mr Busfield and Mr Esah.

Tony Janssens, as he was known, the Chairman, was awarded the Knight of the Order of St Gregory the Great. The papal bull and medals were presented to Anthony Janssens by His Eminence Cardinal Basil Hume OSB. He was associated with the hospital for 25 years and died in 1984 aged 71. A crab apple tree was planted in his memory and is situated in the foreground of the Chapel and has a metal plate with his name on it in commemoration.

Sr Clare O'Driscoll was Orthopaedic Sister Tutor and regularly had a 100% pass rate for her nursing students in the final exams. Sr Louise was in charge of theatres during the 1970s and Sr Pauline was Ward Sister on St Anne's Ward.

In 1978, the combined amounts from the darts league and the garden fete provided more than enough to construct a new hospital shop and to renovate the recreation hall, the first permanent shop for some 30 years.

Left: Sr Mary Joseph (far left), Sr Pauline, Sr Christine and Sr Carmel (far right).

Below: The darts league.

Eastcote darts players raise £4,300—see page 12

With the appeal launched, the building work started; the new rehabilitation centre is in the early stages of construction. Molly Ward, physiotherapy superintendent, Sr Carmel and Pam Wallis, head of occupational therapy, inspect the building.

Other significant contributors to St Vincent's included the Northwood and Eastcote Football Clubs, the Lions Club of Ruislip, Lyons Social Club Greenford, the Queensmead Leisure Centre, the North Harrow Townswomen's Guild and the Inner Wheel of Ruislip and Northwood, Coteford Primary School, Hillside Junior School, St Helen's School and the Woodman public house.

As 1978 was the International Year of the Child, it was especially heartening to see all the support from local schools.

St Vincent's always aimed to support and provide as much for the staff as was possible and the recreation facilities included a tennis court, badminton, table tennis and photography. Students and staff were encouraged to make use of the swimming baths, which were conveniently near.

Many of the former 'boys' of St Vincent's became employees and remained very much the fabric of St Vincent's. Hugh Raciti, or Rac as he was known, came to St Vincent's as a young boy suffering with tuberculosis of the spine.

He managed the staff salaries for over 30 years, for the most part single handed. He was extremely conscientious and meticulous in his work and he was much missed by colleagues and friends when he died.

Mrs Ferguson SRN SCM ONC worked at St Vincent's for 20 years as the Sister in charge in the surgical block and then transferring to the outpatient department. She died suddenly at the hospital in 1977 and the widespread grief and shock at her sudden death indicated a great tribute to her. She would be remembered with great affection and gratitude.

Cardinal Basil Hume and Miss Olive Bacon.

Official Opening

by

His Eminence

Cardinal George Basil Hume, OSB

Archbishop of Westminster

of

NEW REHABILITATION CENTRE
and NEW BUILDINGS

at

**St.Vincent's Orthopaedic
Hospital**

Tuesday, September 9th, 1980

Above left: Official programme for the new rehabilitation wing, 1980.

Above right and below left and right: Cardinal Basil Hume and Anthony Janssens, 1980.

St Vincent's always seemed to have a building appeal in progress and 1979 was no exception. The redevelopment of the rehabilitation centre (physiotherapy and occupational therapy) was a significant project. Alongside this, new pre- and post-operative wards and an extension to the private wing was underway – a major capital project estimated at £300,000.

On Tuesday 9 September 1980, His Eminence Cardinal George Basil Hume OSB formally opened a new rehabilitation centre and new buildings at St Vincent's. The Cardinal went on to say:

As a Trustee of St Vincent's Hospital, I am delighted that this fine institution with its dedicated and expert staff is to have the new facilities it deserves. The decision to build, before costs rise even faster, has been taken. All that remains is for admirers of the hospital's great work of healing, and its exemplary care for those who cannot be healed, to give this appeal their immediate and generous support.

The opening of the buildings was described as 'the culmination of an act of faith, for the work was started as soon as the decision to improve and extend our facilities was made'. Because of the love and respect in which St Vincent's was held, and the admiration of the work carried out in the hospital, the Trustees and Board were sure that the money would be found.

Left: Sr Carmel Cussen DC and Cardinal Basil Hume.

Below: Occupational therapy.

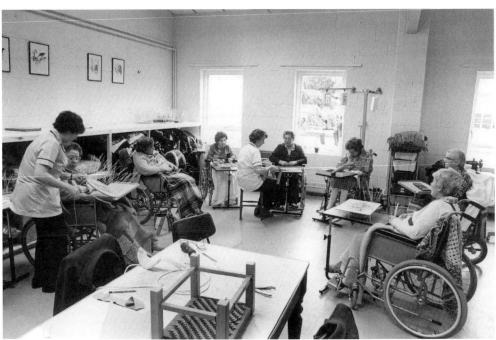

ST VINCENT'S PRAYER GROUP

St Vincent's was going through a particularly difficult time when the Prayer Group was started some time in the early 1980s. The idea came from a few different people and eventually Isabel Rodgers and Sr Carmel worked together to set up the group.

Isabel's husband Peter Rodgers, who was a Board Member at the time, gave his full support and was a very faithful member of the group together with about 20 people from the local parishes.

The main focus was always prayer for St Vincent's and for its future. The group met in the Chapel at 8pm on the first and third Tuesday of every month. Alongside that group we also had a small Adoration Group that came to the Chapel at midday on a Friday once a month. The Chapel bell was always rung at noon and 6pm daily by one of the Sisters. The group continued until the Sisters were withdrawn from St Vincent's in 2003 while the future was being decided.

MEDICAL AND SURGICAL STAFF

St Vincent's kept pace with changes around the world and was a pioneer in the development of orthopaedics within the United Kingdom. The medical and surgical teams were distinguished consultants who have all gone on to share the skills and knowledge developed and learned at St Vincent's.

Justin Howse FRCS, orthopaedic surgeon for the Royal Ballet.

Most notable are: Mr McCrae Aitken the first Honorary Consultant, who retired in 1948; Mr Robert Jones, who led the way in many orthopaedic procedures; Mr Howse, who was the Ballet de Corps surgeon; Dr Gumpel a leading rheumatologist; Paul Strickland, who made significant changes in radiography and is now immortalised with the Paul Strickland Centre at Mount Vernon Hospital in Northwood. Dr Brailsford, radiologist, visited St Vincent's weekly for many years and also worked at the Brompton Hospital and Great Ormond Street Hospital for Sick Children. Anaesthetists were also committed to St Vincent's, in particular Dr Eve Hammer and Dr Betty Milledge.

St Vincent's hosted many orthopaedic medical events over the years; in 1982 ABC Club members were recipients of travelling fellowships to America and Canada awarded by the President of the British Orthopaedic Association. This meeting, which was attended by surgeons from all over the UK, was introduced and chaired by Mr John Crawford Adams. Speakers included:

Dr R. Kelly	Dr Paul Strickland
Mr George Braddock	Mr K. Esah
Mr Peter Busfield	Mr D. Williams
Mr J. Barrie Phillips	Mr D. Hunt
Miss Anne Stotter	Mr A. Howse

In 1982 Mr Robert Mackenny FRCS and Mr W. Bodey FRCS joined the staff and spent many happy years working at St Vincent's. Dr Philip Rassa was the lead radiologist.

The hospital boasted a significant medical faculty, and a number of eminent physicians and surgeons were well-known to St Vincent's and contributed to the high quality of care and innovation over the years, alongside the expert care of the Sisters of Charity and the nursing team. The surgeons included Mr Jayabalan, Mr Ram and Mr Phillips, to name a few.

Justin Howse FRCS was one of the many notable surgeons. He was the foremost orthopaedic surgeon to the dance world and the preserver of many a stellar performing career, including those of Margot Fonteyn and Judi Dench.

RESIDENT STAFF:

Nurses: 38, non-resident: 12 (including physiotherapists)
Male staff: 32, non-resident: 13
Female staff: 25, non-resident: 3
One priest
One doctor

ORTHOPAEDIC NURSE TRAINING

The beginnings of professional nursing and nurse education did not emerge until the second half of the 19th century. Before then nursing was not recognised as a profession and nurses and domestic servants were interchangeable.

St Vincent's had a proud and prestigious past as an education establishment.

Orthopaedic nursing aims were, even in the very early days, about focusing on the individual and ensuring that they regained as much mobility as possible or supporting them adapting to changes in their life following injury or disease. The rapid developments in orthopaedic surgery and rehabilitation have been paralleled by the changes to nursing. Where at one time someone with TB would be confined to bed for up to a year or more now most people are managed in the community. Orthopaedic nursing has always been at the forefront of holistic care – care for the person as a whole – and this is evident throughout the story here so far. Engaging the children in 'normal' life activities and not discriminating between those who were 'up boys' and those who were 'bed boys' is one example.

Developments in orthopaedic surgery meant that the provision for caring for people on long-term bed rest was also improved. The wholesale use of traction to support muscle spasm and ensure that bone healing could be encouraged with the limb in alignment was a significant change and has only in the past few years become a dying art.

Orthopaedic nursing was developed in part due to the profession as a whole wishing to focus on 'specialists' to care for patients in medical model fields such as renal nursing, ophthalmology and emergency medicine. The General Nursing Council created national boards for each country and the English National Boards in turn developed the speciality courses. For orthopaedic nursing the course was called the Orthopaedic Nursing Certificate (ONC), a 12-month course, at one time for nurses who were already on the GNC register.

TRACTION

Care of patients in traction is quite straightforward and the aspect of care that needed to be considered was mainly that of caring for someone on bed rest. However, the appearance of traction to the uninitiated could appear a conundrum, especially if it was a Thomas splint with its compound block pulleys.

The plaster bed was often suspended using compound pulleys. Two overhead frames joined together by transverse bars were also required. The plaster shell was attached to a wooden frame, one cross-bar being below the shoulders and the other level with the knees.

Many children in St Vincent's were on plaster beds for many months and credit was given to the nursing staff for ensuring that the young patients were so well looked after. Long periods of inactivity created many nursing challenges, not least poor skin, digestive problems, constipation and low mood. Diversion tactics and essentially good old-fashioned nursing care was one of the greatest assets St Vincent's cherished.

PLASTER OF PARIS

Plaster of Paris has been used since early Egyptian times, originally for wall decorations. It is made of gypsum, a naturally occurring mineral. The name, plaster of Paris ostensibly originates from an accident to a house built on a deposit of gypsum near Paris. The house burned down, and when rain fell on the baked mud of the floors it was noted that footprints in the mud set rock hard.

This led to the rediscovery of the practice of heating gypsum to make a smooth covering for walls. The use of plaster of Paris applied to a continuous bandage in order to immobilise fractures was first credited to a Dutch army surgeon, Antonius Mathysen (1805–78). These bandages were made by rubbing dry plaster of Paris powder into coarsely woven cotton bandages, which were then soaked in water before being applied. Prior to the commercial availability of such bandages in 1931, this was the only method of production.

Plaster of Paris is still used but only in a limited amount and has been replaced by lightweight casting materials which are better for the patient and easier to manage.

NURSE'S TRAINING AND MASSAGE SCHOOL

Applicants must be over 17 years of age and have a good education. The course for nurses lasts two years, at the end of which time a certificate will be given to those who successfully pass their examination, this is for orthopaedic nursing only, but includes theatre and plaster work, post operative treatment, ward management and treatment of crippling diseases.

This advert was written in 1930 for applicants to the training held at St Vincent's Orthopaedic Hospital.

The School of Nursing opened in 1947 – the NHS was inaugurated in 1948. With the creation of the National Health Service nursing education increasingly diverged from the traditional model of in-service training on the wards.

In 1950 the General Nursing Council decided that the Pinner affiliation could continue until the new bill was thoroughly working and St Vincent's

Sr Angela Murray as Nurse Tutor.

could continue to train students and send them on to the affiliated hospitals of St John's and Elizabeth and Royal National Orthopaedic Hospitals.

As part of the review that St Vincent's undertook to ensure it was fit to remain a teaching centre the records identify at that time there was the following:

Patients: adults 65, children 100
Sisters (Daughters of Charity): 19 resident

The Orthopaedic Nursing Certificate (ONC) was a pre-registration course of 20 months' duration, which was taken by the majority of students in St Vincent's. The candidates were able to start at 17 years and the minimum requirements was four GCE O levels with A, B, or C grades.

Successful candidates then proceeded to a shortened State Registered Nurse (SRN) training in a general hospital. Once they qualified and worked as a nurse for 12 months they could add ONC to their qualification in recognition of the pre-nursing course.

The Diploma in Orthopaedic Nursing was a two-year course similar to the certificate, available for State Enrolled Nurses (SEN). More often than not St Vincent's achieved a 100% pass rate and often came top of the UK in the examinations – this excellent reputation was a sure testament of the dedication and skill of the tutors.

One year ten nursing students participated in the Ruislip Northwood 20th Festival, an annual event for verse and public speaking. They enjoyed this immensely and achieved high marks.

Sr Clare O'Driscoll DC was the lead tutor and ensured that the students gave first-rate clinical care. Sr Clare was very popular and her enthusiasm for orthopaedics and providing good care was infectious.

ST VINCENT'S HOSPITAL
(Under the care of the Sisters of Charity of St Vincent de Paul)

This is to Certify that

....

has completed a Course of Orthopaedic Nursing and successfully passed the Hospital Final Examination

Matron

Date   *Examiners*

Orthopaedic nursing certificate.

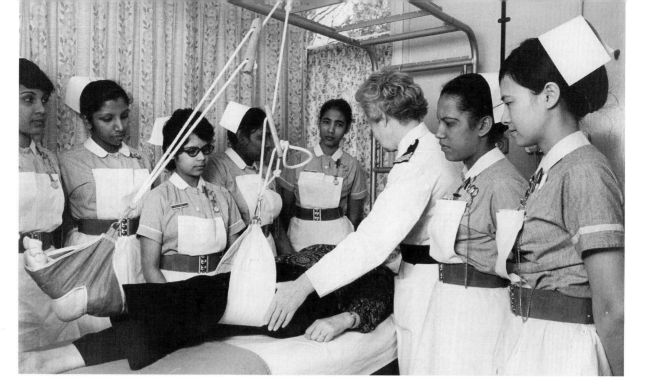

Mrs McNeil and the students being taught the principles of traction.

Anne Warren SRN ONC joined the teaching staff in 1977 and Irene Heywood Jones SRN RMN DN RNT commenced as a part-time tutor in 1978 and completed her ONC in 1982.

Fr Peter was the only male nurse to undertake the Diploma in Orthopaedic Nursing under the tuition of Sr Clare O'Driscoll in 1985:

> My time at the hospital was very happy and I am still in contact with the Sisters through Sr Mary Jo Powell, whose family I have known for over 40 years. I am told I was the one and only male nurse to train at St Vincent's.
>
> I nursed for over 27 years until my calling to the priesthood and eventual ordination in July 2000 for the Diocese of Leeds. I am now the parish priest in Cleckheaton, West Yorkshire. A friend once said to me 'from bedpans to dog collar' when he got to know what I was about to undertake. I am so blessed in my ministry.

The completion of the ENB 941 Elderly Care Course in December 1996 was the last formal course held in the hospital. Not ever wishing to end – the education centre was then made over to a conference centre for the local homes and community to use.

Post-basic education during the 1990s made a transition to centres of higher education and universities and so changed the face of nursing forever. As part of this metamorphic change, St Vincent's took the decision to end formal education after 49 years.

Left: Sr Clare O'Driscoll DC.

Below: The official opening of the School of Nursing building, 1970.

Summary of Miss Sayer's visit to St Vincent's Hospital (July12,13,14.)
1976

On the above dates the hospital was inspected on behalf of the G.N.C. by
Miss Sayer who has previously inspected us on two occasions. Miss Sayer's
routine visit was precipitated somewhat by the problem presented to our nursing
school by the closure of H.C.W. and the consequent lack of paediatric experience
for our pupil nurses.
      An informal meeting was held on the morning of the close
of the visit at which Miss Roker(Regional Nurse Training comm.) Miss Tucker
(C.N.O. Education Hillingdon Area.) Miss Byatt, A.N.O. Mr Turner (representing
the board of governors) Sister Clare, Sister Carmel, Mr Carne and myself were
present. Mr Phillips, representing the surgeons was availabe, but not actually
present at the discussion. Mrs Warren, allocations officer for St Vincent's also
attended. Miss Sayer informed us she would consult her committee, but she
could be sure of some aspects of their decisions in view of her findings, their
report will not be available until late September.

Miss Sayer commenced by assuring us she was very satisfied both with the
quality of nursing care, the good spirit evident throughout the hospital, and the
dynamic approach to teaching evidenced by Sr. Clare and by all the ward
sisters in their turn. However, she found not only the absence of paediatric
experience, but also some deficiency in the departmental experience available.
She is in little doubt that the approval for our S.E.N. training school
will be withdrawn. We are of course committed to our next intake of pupils
(in November) and during the ensuing period the arrangements made
for clinic attendance, and possibly some further help from Miss Tucker
at Hillingdon will satisfy the requrements. She looked very carefully at
St Mary's ward, and while finding it a very good unit, doing admirable
work, she did not feel that it could be regarded as a substitute for
geriatric experience, but should be viewed as a speciality in its own
right. To second our nurses for any further period than is now the case
would be totally undesirable.
      With regard to the future of the hospital in relation to
nurse training, we will continue as an O.N.C. training hospital and it is
hoped that if sufficient extra candidates apply in the future we may be
able to extend the numbers in each school. This will be dependant upon
approval by the J.E.Board, the authority responsible for Orthopaedic
certificates. The problem of no children patients affects this somewhat
but we are awaiting Miss Elliott's approval of our interim arrangements.
One thing is certain, to retain the approval of our hospital as an O.N.C.
training school, 100 beds are minimally required, and we would need to
look at an alternative use for H.C.W. speedily. I would ask Dr Hammer
to consult her colleagues on the matter of any suggestions they may have,
as I know that Mr Braddock and Mr Phillips have both expressed the view that
they could use more beds for their other waiting lists, and I would hope
we could help by taking an increased number of post.-op. or post. trauma
transfers.

Sister Gertrude.   The above information should not make any very
immediate difference to the sisters' presence here. if at all. It must
however be looked at in relation to our own problems of personnel in the
community; and the present financial climate in the health service makes
increased provision in any area unlikely. However there is no need fo
immediateanxiety; and I will keep you informed of future developments,
as far as I am able. Within the hospital, it is felt that this must all
be considered and re-discussed at intervals. One can no longer just
tide over from crisis point to crisis point, but try to evaluate
possibilities and plan ahead. Mr Turner, a very balanced and very
enthusiastic member of our hospital board said to me after the meeting that
he wonders if this is the writing on the wall!

Sister Elizabeth D.C.

GMC Nursing Inspection Report to St Vincent's, 1976.

Above left: Rev. Peter Smith, parish priest, Leeds Diocese.

Above right: Staff who worked at St Vincent's. Left to right: Violetta Laraya, Sr Carmel, Irene Heywood Jones, Sr Clare and Joan Woodington, 1990.

A MARRIAGE MADE IN HEAVEN

Irene Heywood Jones recalls how she came to be involved with St Vincent's:

I was sitting in Eastcote with my new baby, recently having given up my job as a nurse tutor at St Bernard's Hospital, and was desperate to find part-time work. Tom Connell knew me, and his wife Petal was night sister at St Vincent's, where they were looking for a nurse tutor to help Sister Clare.

Bingo. After my interview with Sister Carmel and Clare they gained a qualified nurse tutor to cover when Clare taught at Hillingdon, as part of the arrangement with the Health Authority. My Perena was happily ensconced with a wonderful childminder and I was back working for two days in the job I loved, although I had no previous knowledge of the 'the little hospital up on the hill'.

As my knowledge was insufficient to tackle the specialist subject, I taught basic nursing care and anatomy and physiology with the 17-year-old pre-registration students, largely comprising young girls from Guyana, Mauritius and the Philippines. Sister Clare and I made a well-balanced team, together with our gem of a secretary, Joan Woodington, who kept the wheels oiled in the School of Nursing. Heaven only knows what these shy girls, thrown into new work in a new 'cold' country made of a garrulous Irish nun and a crazy young tutor who told them to 'give the patient a good wash, nurse, she isn't made of porcelain!' I was maybe a little challenging with the 'experiential learning' but if you can expect a patient to sit on a bedpan, I believe it only right that you practise balancing on one yourself.

But we must have done something right because we regularly got 100% pass rate. The girls were diligent at their studies and practical work, thrived in a small, family-like community while far from home. They lived in the Nurses' Home, could enjoy the countryside and could get to the lights of London.

So they were not averse to Sister Clare's pleas when a shift needed covering due to sickness and, of course, being senior in the hospital, meant Sister was able to negotiate their day off in lieu. We miss that personal, flexible type of management and reciprocity in larger organisations.

The pre-registration courses eventually ceased and from 1982 we then only took qualified nurses to be trained in the speciality of orthopaedic nursing. I had a second baby, took a short maternity leave, studied for the exam and passed my Orthopaedic Nursing Certificate (with honours), ready to teach on the more concentrated one-year course.

I was an established member of the RCN (Royal College of Nursing) Orthopaedics Society and edited the newsletter, with fabulous 'boney' men drawings by Barbara Christopher. Here I also met Jacquie Scott, who coincidentally lived in Eastcote and had worked briefly as a staff nurse at St Vincent's in 1979.

Changes in nurse education nationally meant that orthopaedic training eventually ceased and at this point the religious community decided to move Sr Clare to work at St David's Home for ex-servicemen in Ealing. I took up the baton to organise Elderly Care Course ENB 941, which ran for about five years, providing training for nurses working in elderly care units or care homes.

I also completed a master's degree at Brunel University. When it was decided to close the School of Nursing it happened to coincide with the retirement of Sr Christine Wholley DC and so after 20 years away from the bedside I found myself being coerced into becoming the outpatients manager.

I was involved in the protracted tendering for orthopaedic services for the area when funding changed for us and was then a threat to the future of St Vincent's – it was a stressful time for all.

Eventually our lovely kind, safe service, so beloved by local people, was taken from us and the hospital had to be closed. I stayed working in the area and keeping close connections and interest in the new nursing home.

Everyone remembers the annual fete and none more than my children, who always came along to 'help'. I never joined the 'cake 'n' bake' brigade but was in my element on the second-hand clothes stall – and that was a regular 'bun fight'.

So to my clinical colleagues I raise my little frilly cap in admiration for your contribution over the years in giving professional and empathic service: Florence Symes, Sylvia Watson, Jenny Yexley, Maureen Eaton, to mention a few, and in the OPD 'the fun team': Annie Hood, Sheila Griffith, Andrea Hill, Diane May, and Karen. Sr Pauline DC and Sr Christine DC were formidable Sisters in their places of work and frightened those early little nurses, but were honestly kind and compassionate people to anyone.

I am also happy to take a little credit for reintroducing Jacquie Scott to the hospital as a possible successor to Sr Carmel. It was a rubbish move for Jacquie, who within a year of appointment, keen to put SVH orthopaedics firmly on the map, found herself scooping up people facing redundancy.

But it was the absolute best move for St Vincent's. Jacquie put her heart and soul into the place which had achieved such a prestigious history and she, with John Davern and Alan Edmondson, must be credited with the tremendous effort required to get such a top-notch nursing home built, up and running.

Not one for any formal religion, working with the 'nunny buns' sounded a bit unlikely and it caused quite a stir among my friends. However, this flamboyant, noisy, atheist/humanist got on like a house on fire with the lovely nuns, because I know goodness within people, whatever religion it is wrapped up in (and I suspect they saw my goodness beyond the brash exterior).

From 'bin' to 'Vin', my belief was that fate/destiny/serendipity brought us all together …

Irene Heywood Jones and Jacquie Scott were founder members of the Society of Orthopaedic Nursing within the Royal College of Nursing. Irene was the editor of the magazine *Bare Bones* and Jacquie organised many National conferences for the London group. Both nurses were contributors to *Nursing Times* and in 1994 collaborated with the magazine and KCI Medical to organise and judge a competition for an orthopaedic nursing care study.

LEAGUE OF FRIENDS

The League of Friends was founded in 1981. A committee was formed, a constitution approved, the charitable status required. New members of the league were always being sought, and almost all skills were put to good use somewhere within the hospital. Membership was 100 and some 950 people were life members. During this time the funds raised averaged around £5,000 annually. The appeal was in effect the catalyst for the formation of the League of Friends of St Vincent's Hospital which was registered as a charity in its own right on 4 November 1981 with the stated objects 'to help patients and former patients of the St Vincent's Orthopaedic Hospital who are sick, convalescent, disabled, handicapped, infirm or in need of financial assistance and generally, to support the charitable work of the said hospital'.

It focused particularly on the services within the hospital such as the shop, gardening and comforts; its members were unpaid volunteers. The League of Friends raised an average of £25,000 a year.

League of Friends' great fundraisers, Doug Hannam and Nick Cutcliffe.

The league was officially de-registered as a charity in 2008 but in its near 27 years of existence had raised many thousands of pounds to help towards the work of St Vincent's.

Among those connected with work of the league during its time in existence were: John Young, Peter Cloot, Dora Lockett, Rose Barr, Peter Hoskins, Elaine and Brian Dunks, Patrick Helharman, Pam Parkhurst, Annie Secunda, Irene and Llewellyn Heywood Jones, Sr Mary Jo Powell, Sr Catherine Langdon, Jacquie Scott, Colin Furness, Ray Plummer and many more.

The hospital was not short of fundraising efforts and significant efforts were made to secure funds. The two appeal directors, Nick Cutcliffe and Doug Hannam, ensured they kept focused and were responsible for ensuring the hospital kept out of debt, and St Vincent's owes a great debt of gratitude to their remarkable work.

The original committee members included Nick Cutcliffe, Doug Hannam, John Young, Vic Middlemiss, Eric Middlemiss, Pauline Turner, Dora Lockett, Muriel Parkes, Peter Hoskins, Rose Barr, Sr Mary Jo Powell, and Sr Catherine Langdon.

The annual Christmas tree sale was a tradition for many local residents and staff, held the two weekends before Christmas, no matter what the weather. People came from miles to choose their tree for the festive period, a profit accruing of around £1,200.

The fete committee, led by Tom McManamon, Chairman, Anne Reid and a party of volunteers from the Pinner parish, stayed outside the League of Friends and was a very successful group of volunteers.

At its peak, the league had a membership of well in excess of 1,200 members and volunteers donated their time as well as raising vast sums of money through the Annual Garden Fete, Christmas tree sales, car boot sales and the Alexandra Rose Day.

FUNDRAISING

Donations over the years were quite significant and St Vincent's ensured that it all went into providing an exemplary service to the local community. By 1981 the net profit had risen to £7,600.

The largest single money-spinner at the fete was the grand draw, which usually had over 50 attractive prizes on offer. It was manned by the Campion Players, an amateur dramatic group from Harrow.

Some of the organisations that spent a significant time fundraising on behalf of St Vincent's include: St Martin's School Northwood; Irish Society of Harrow; Frithwood Primary School, Northwood; Ruislip Round Table; Northwood Grange; Townswomen's Guild; Rosary Priory Bushey Heath; Ruislip/ Northwood Rotary Club; Clay Pigeon Darts League; St Matthew's, Northwood; Northwood Liberal Synagogue; Eastbury Farm School Mummers; Pinner Ladies' Circle; Harrow Young Musicians; Ealing Police; King Edward Hospital Fund for London; Metropolitan Hospital Sunday Fund; Swakeleys' Home Guard (1944) Association; Union of Communication Workers; Not Quite Perfect Golf Society of Northwood; Independent Order of Foresters; Studio School, Pinner and the Knights of St Columba.

Individuals included: the famous tenor, Thomas Round, who held a concert at St Helen's School Northwood, and ex-patient Douglas Cameron, who made the Easter Sunday Good Cause radio appeal which raised £4,438.

To raise the £300,000 needed, an appeal organisation was set up and an appeal committee formed. The 35 members undertook to make approaches to trusts, companies and organisations with whom they had personal connections. The target of £300,000 was eventually exceeded in July 1982 when an anonymous gift of £40,000 pushed the appeal total to £318,163.

Fundraising.

STATISTICS FOR YEAR TO 31st MARCH, 1980

IN-PATIENTS

Number of Beds and In-Patients

	Twelve months to 31st March, 1980	Twelve months to 31st March, 1979
BEDS		
Complement to 31st March, 1980	123	123
Average daily complement	123	123
Average daily number closed owing to:		
Closure of Ward...	1	1
Average daily number open	122	122
Average daily number occupied	78	83
Number of In-Patients in the Hospital at 1st April, 1979 ... 86		
Number of In-Patients admitted	1196	1180
Number of In-Patients in Hospital at 31st March, 1980 ... 91		
Average number of days each patient was resident...	24	26
Number of Patients admitted and discharged who were resident for:		
Two and three days	130	132
Only one day	61	57

OUT-PATIENTS

Numbers

			Twelve months to 31st March, 1980
Total number of new Out-Patients:	Hospital Clinics	...	1,280
Total number of attendances:	Hospital Clinics	...	11,271

WORK DONE IN SPECIAL DEPARTMENTS

Number of X-ray Examinations	4,945
Treatments: Hospital Clinics	32,787
Number of Operations performed	969

Business activity, 1980.

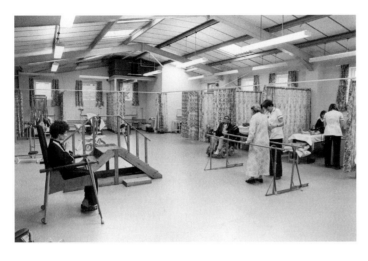

Left: Physiotherapy gym.

Below: League of Friends logo.

League of Friends of St Vincent's Orthopaedic Hospital
Eastcote, Pinner, Middlesex HA5 2NB Tel: 081 866 0151

Often you heard people say, 'for us as a family once we had bought the tree from St Vincent's we felt Christmas had arrived'. The customary tree sale continued after the hospital closed until, sadly, the supplier for the trees passed away, thus ending a long tradition.

The development of the hospital saw investment in the catering department providing services to both patients and staff. The occupational therapy department comprised a team of three – two qualified practitioners and a full-time occupational therapy assistant, Juliette Hurran. After further training Juliette returned to St Vincent's Nursing Home in 2006 as a valued activities co-ordinator. She has been associated with St Vincent's for many years.

The hospital also boasted a social work team seconded by the London Borough of Hillingdon, which was very effective in supporting many patients.

Annual Garden Fete

Without exception, each raconteur spoke of the famous fete held at St Vincent's, a tradition common in country hospitals. Held annually on August Bank Holiday Saturday (except during the war), the fundraising effort was a notable calendar event in the locality. Besides being enormous fun for the patients, staff, Sisters and friends, it welcomed people of the local community to ensure a wonderfully enjoyable and profitable day.

It began in 1941 and over the years grew like Topsy. The hospital site was given over, with a miniature railway, dog show, flower display in the Chapel, beer tent, jumble sale, and in the recreation hall, teas and cakes prepared by staff and Sisters labouring for days over tray bakes. The house doctor took 10 pence a pop to take your blood pressure and high spots were the copious bottle tombola and the maddening search for the one key to release that bottle of whisky. Cadet groups came with musicians, police came with dogs and fire service with their fire engine.

Donations of goods were generous and plentiful, both from individuals and organisations such as schools and churches.

The hospital always managed to secure notable people to declare the fete open, including some seriously famous personalities who took an interest in supporting charities for the disabled.

Jessie Matthews was one of Britain's greatest film and stage stars of the 1930s and played Mrs Dale in the radio series *Mrs Dale's Diary*. She was a great friend of St Vincent's and supported many events, especially the annual fete. Jessie chose to end her days at St Vincent's and sadly died of cancer in 1981. Her ashes are interred at St Martin's Church, Ruislip. Her cousin Anne (Nancy) Simons, who worked on the switchboard at St Vincent's, was at her side when she died.

Jessie left her favourite cousin all her personal scrapbooks, photo albums and her famous red-and-gold *This is Your Life* book from her appearance on the television show. Eventually she sold Jessie's memorabilia to an anonymous buyer, later to be revealed as Sir Andrew Lloyd Webber, who at the time was making a television programme of Jessie Matthews' life.

St Vincent's continued to be championed by numerous organisations and local clubs who worked diligently throughout the year to ensure the annual fete and other events were well supported.

Help also came from the darts players of Ruislip, Northwood and Eastcote, known as the St Vincent's Darts League, who made their first donation of £100 in 1958 and went from strength to strength donating in the region of £2,000 annually. Thanks mainly to their generosity every ward was fitted with a patient/nurse alarm system.

Tom Baldwin and Stephen Lovell were always at the forefront and would be seen preparing the grounds each year.

Tom was part of the gardening team led by Charlie Carey during the good years at St Vincent's. He was a friendly young man who had some unusual ideas! Recently someone reminded me that Tom had a habit of stopping at any glass doors or windows to comb his hair, using the glass as a mirror.

When financial problems hit St Vincent's the gardening team was reduced. Anyone who retired or left was not replaced. Eventually Tom alone remained out of the group and kept the grounds in very good shape. He swept up leaves, cleared paths of snow almost as soon as it fell and took great pride in keeping everything in order.

Above left: Jessie Matthews and Nick Cutcliffe.

Above right: Tom Baldwin (holding the ladder) and Stephen Lovell prepare the grounds for an event.

He did not have a great knowledge of the skills required for actual garden-ing but did not like weeds growing. One particular day there were some very beautiful sweet peas growing in large containers. Sadly by evening the flowers had faded. We wondered why. Tom eventually told us he had passed that morning with some weedkiller spray and it was a bit windy! He was well known and loved by everyone at St Vincent's. His jokes were famous. He loved to tell new staff not to worry; the first ten years are the worst!

Stephen worked on the maintenance team. He did so many jobs for all depart-ments in the hospital with a gracious efficiency. He was very knowledgeable and of a quiet disposition. He had a great sense of humour and we all shared lots of jokes with him. Stephen had a great talent for photography, with many events at the hospital being taken by him. Stephen was always a loyal friend to St Vincent's and a great support in whatever way he could help.

The Knights of Columba and the Ruislip and Northwood Round Tables over the years provided a huge amount of support to St Vincent's, in particular at the Annual Garden Fete. There were a number of characters who used their time and special skills to make so many of the events at St Vincent's successful: Tom McManamon and Frank Hogan and the fete committee significantly reflected the hard work and splendid organisation.

Top: Stephen Lovell and Tom Baldwin.

Above left: Tom Baldwin and Stephen Lovell.

Above right: Vera Lynn signs autographs.

Left: Douglas Bader visits St Vincent's.

On 28 August 1948 the first garden fete to be held for a number of years attracted 3,000 people. They spent most generously, resulting in a cheque for £893 7s 4d for the anticipated building fund. St Vincent's was very grateful to all those who helped to make the fete such a grand success, particularly to Miss Vera Lynn and Mr Charlie Kunz, who came to open it.

Indeed, Vera Lynn continued to lend support to disabled children. She formed a cerebral palsy charity in 1953 called SOS, Stars Organisation for Spastics. In 1992 she founded the Dame Vera Lynn School for Parents and Handicapped Children.

Group Captain Douglas Bader was an inspirational visitor for the patients as he had both legs amputated following a devastating plane crash during aerial aerobatics in 1931. Despite that handicap he spent an illustrious career as a fighter pilot during the war, and later received a knighthood for services to disabled people.

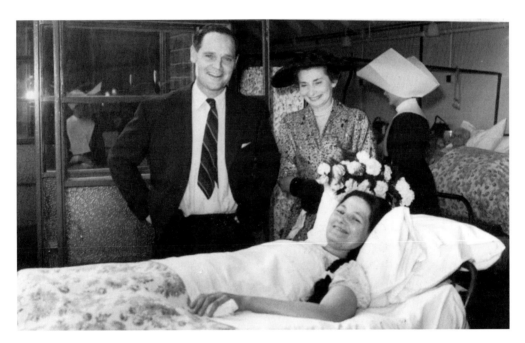

Above: Douglas and Thelma Bader in 1955, visiting the children on the wards.

Left: Douglas Bader and his wife with Fr O'Daly and a young boy.

Left: Donkey Derby, 1955.

Below: Donkey Derby on fete day, 1950s.

Bottom: Miss Hopper (radiographer) and the children enjoying the horse show at the Garden Fete, 1948.

Above left: Garden Fete, 1964.

Above right: Lesley Murray, aged four, riding the switch-back railway.

Below: Switch-back railway and the nurses.

Douglas Bader opened the Annual Garden Fete in 1955, which raised a record £1,391. There was so much going on during that year, with a Donkey Derby one of the favourite attractions.

Branches of the Knights of St Columba joined forces at the fete to provide over a dozen different stalls. Other organisations included the Ruislip Lions and the Round Tables from Pinner and Northwood. Over 200 people were involved on the day, including the Sisters manning stalls. St Gabriel's Youth Club from South Harrow were manning all the sideshows on the lawn.

Above left: Pat Hagan at one of the fetes – her father worked in the workshops.

Above right: Dragon train from the Northwood Round Table.

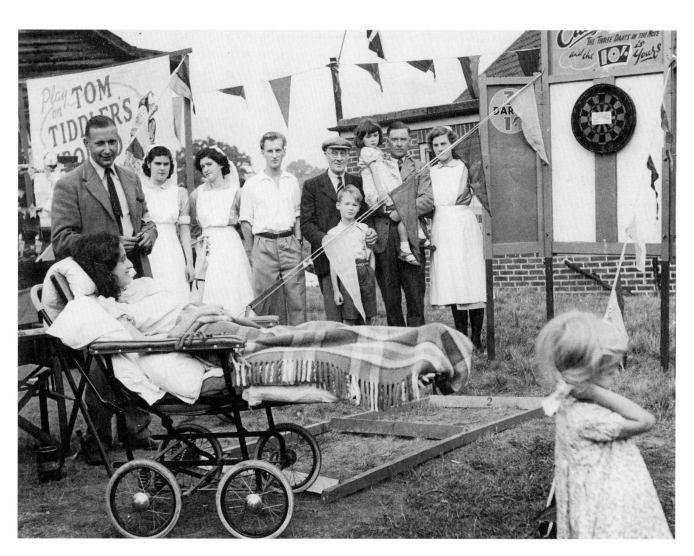

Garden Fete, 1950s.

Mr Powell, who had deformed hands, had a display of matchstick models. Sr Frances Bayley DC used to clean any valuables and take them to a shop in Pinner to sell to raise money for the fete fund.

The fete was always opened by a celebrity if possible, remembering Squadron Leader Douglas Bader, Vera Lynn, Charlie Kunz, Tommy Steele, Honourable Mayors and Mayoress of Hillingdon, Frank Williams from *Dad's Army* and *You Rang M'Lord* in 1994 and Bob Holness, who eventually became a welcome resident of the new St Vincent's Nursing Home. The annual fete for 1978 was opened by Betty Thorndike, Mayor of Hillingdon, and in 1979 was opened by Councillor Leonard Lally, Mayor of Hillingdon.

Above left: Charlie Kunz, musician.

Above right: Fete day: Mayor Betty Thorndike, Sr Carmel Cussen DC and Sr Paula Kearon DC in her usual fete day pitch on the patio.

Left: Sr Theodora DC, who once ran the outpatients department.

Top: Freehand drawing by an ex-patient of the crucifix under the Holm Oak.

Above left: Moira Newman, Kevin Sharratt and Marie Nutgens.

Above right: Stallholders: Margaret Bayliss (left) and Joyce White.

Left: Peggy Davern, Isobel Rodgers, Peter Cloot, John Davern, Ray Plummer and Vic Middlemiss.

FAMOUS VISITORS TO ST VINCENT'S

Charlie Kunz was one of many entertainers that made time to visit St Vincent's. He was an American-born British musician popular during the British dance band era. Charlie had also been a patient at St Vincent's and knew the hospital well.

He was such a distinctive and popular pianist that he abandoned his orchestra to concentrate on his piano playing, both at music hall venues and on the BBC. Two of Britain's most famous female vocalists were with his orchestra in the 1930s: Vera Lynn and songstress Dorothy Squires.

Jimmy Edwards and his beautiful singing star Yana, from the London panto-mime *Cinderella*, made a flying unannounced visit to St Vincent's to entertain the children in 1959.

They had a fun afternoon, cracked jokes, danced and the troupe of performing dogs went through their paces, rounded off when Jimmy played a tune on his euphonium and generally got the children and patients into high spirits.

Earlier that week rock star Tommy Steele had visited for a sing-song. He was accompanied by his fiancée, brought his guitar and sang and played lots of popular songs to the children, then walked around the wards speaking to the bedridden patients.

Fete day, 1998: entertaining in the 'old orchard'.

Above: Jimmy Edwards at St Vincent's, 1959.

Right: Jimmy Edwards and the cast from the London pantomime *Cinderella* pay a flying visit to St Vincent's (Courtesy of *Ruislip-Northwood Post*, 1959).

Below: Tommy Steele and the cast of 'Cinderella' perform for the patients.

Top Marks For John Says Jimmy Edwards

Full marks for that boy for a very sharp piece of detecting. John Allan Godfrey went to St. Vincent's Hospital, Eastcote on Sunday afternoon to visit brother Peter when he stopped and stared at a very familiar figure striding down the corridor. The mortarboard and gown coupled with that walrus like moustache gave the game away. It was none other than Britain's top laughter maker — Jimmy Edwards.

Jimmy, beautiful singing star Yana and a host of the cast from the London pantomime "Cinderella" paid a flying visit to the hospital to give the authorities some money collected from weekly raffles run by the boys and girls of the chorus. They failed to bring the cash, promised to send it on shortly but entertained the children to a quick fire show instead.

They danced, sang and cracked jokes and a troupe of performing dogs went through their paces but the afternoon was only made complete when Jimmy Edwards entertained them on his euphonium.

The advance party arrived at the hospital on Friday in the form of rock 'n' roll singing star Tommy Steele and his fiancee. Tommy showed the children some films and played his guitar and sang numbers the children requested.

His visit had been kept top secret as the hospital ground have no gates and the authoritie feared for the safety of thei patients if the word got round that the rock idol was in th district.

TOMMY STEELE AND PANTO CAST PLAY TO PATIENTS

Goodwill Christmas tree plan

EASTCOTE Community Association is planning to put up a "goodwill" Christmas tree in the district next December to help raise funds for a local charity. The tree, the largest obtainable at the time, will be illuminated and set up in a

PATIENTS, including children at St. Vincent's Hospital, Northwood, had an exciting time last week when the principals and cast of the pantomime, Cinderella, now playing at the Coliseum, visited the hospital and provided impromptu entertainment.

The first thrill was on Friday, when Tommy Steele, accompanied by his fiancee, brought his guitar and sang and played a lot of popular songs to the children

He then walked around and had a cheery word with bed-ridden patients in the various wards.

On Sunday, as many children as it was possible to move were taken to the largest men's ward, and were entertained by the remainder of the cast.

Jimmy Edwards, complete with cap and gown, played his euphonium and generally got the children and patients in high spirits.

Bruce Trent sang songs from the show, and Yana (Cinde-

Classes may be first in country

RUISLIP - NORTH -

Mr. Hullah Brown, the composer, listens to

Right: Tommy Steele, musician, signing autographs.

Far right: Tommy Steele and his fiancée with Sr Angela Murray.

Below: St Vincent's Nursing Home ambulance.

Sr Mary Neville DC, who was Sister Superior in 1950, would not allow fortune-telling on the site, but anything else was acceptable, such as a bar in the garage and dancing in the evening. The day used to end with a film of St Vincent's shown in the evening, entry fee 2*s* 6*d*.

The local bank manager joined others to count the money in the Sisters' House. Mike Alford and Eric Middlemiss from the League of Friends committee would often be seen planting out the beds for winter and spring displays.

A new ambulance was delivered in February 1982. David Woodward was engaged as the driver and would be booked for patient outings, trips to local hospitals and student nurse educational visits.

In March 1985 the Sisters of Charity marked the centenary of the Daughters in England and the foundation of the British Province by holding an entertaining social evening at St Vincent's to explore the history of both the Daughters and the hospital.

St Vincent's was often in the spotlight when it came to clinical advances and its contribution to the wider community. However behind the scenes there always seemed to be a struggle to ensure that St Vincent's remained financially viable, although it continued to be supported by the Local Health Authority.

ALAN EDMONDSON

Alan Edmondson joined the Board of St Vincent's Hospital in 1978. He succeeded Ben Turner as Chairman of Trustees in 1985. A newspaper article in December 1987 indicated the level of negotiations that were ongoing.

In 1992, to meet an immediate need, Alan assumed responsibility for the day-to-day running of the hospital as its director and general manager. This continued until 1996 when a new general manager was appointed and he resumed membership of the Board. Alan was very much at the forefront of supporting and leading the hospital to ensure that it maintained its charitable status and its reputation as a leading light in orthopaedics. He was very involved with the transition of St Vincent's from a hospital to nursing home in 2006.

NO TRUTH IN RUMOURS

St Vincents won't close says board

Into the 1990s – the final decade.

ST. VINCENT'S Hospital in Pinner may face the threat of closure, it is claimed.

Members of Ruislip Northwood Labour Party claim that they have learnt from 'informed sources' that the future of the orthopaedic hospital is in doubt because Hillingdon Health Authority may withdraw its funding.

Now members of the local party have vowed to oppose any attempt to close it if such a step leads to an overall loss of beds in the area.

Spokesperson Ruth Allan said• "If our worst fears are realised and the district health authority goes ahead with its plans, the Labour Party will lead a campaign to save St Vincent's,

But Allan Edmondson, chairman of the board of managers of St Vincent, has denied the claims that the hospital's future is in doubt and said: "it's not true at all."

He said: "The problem we face is where we go next which has not been settled or determined. There is often a problem of funding from the district health authority, and the problem of whether they can go on using us as before."

He insisted: "St Vincents will not close, it just might change. It's role is being carefully considered."

Sr Simes, St Anne's Ward, 1980s.

Professionally he is a chartered engineer with long experience of operational management and as a company director in the motor industry. He is pleased to continue his long association with St Vincent's as a Member of the Board. He remains a talented and loyal member of the Board of St Vincent's.

– INTO THE 1990S – THE FINAL DECADE –

Orthopaedic surgery was thriving at St Vincent's, with many people benefiting from total hip and knee replacements, back, foot or hand operations.

Judith Walker recalls her Aunt Connie, originally a patient in 1936 with TB, who was many years later admitted for a total hip replacement to ease her discomfort caused by bone secondary deposits from breast cancer. 'Her care was exemplary and the surgery did give her several pain-free months for which we were all thankful.' Judith adds, 'the Sisters of Charity, so rightly named, enhanced our lives and those of countless others in so very many ways. We as a family, have much to thank St Vincent's for.'

The Mayor of Hillingdon adopted St Vincent's as his charity in 1993. As part of the Eastcote Christmas Festival, St Vincent's took part in a charity bed push through the local streets of Eastcote, Ruislip Manor and Ruislip raising significant support and funds.

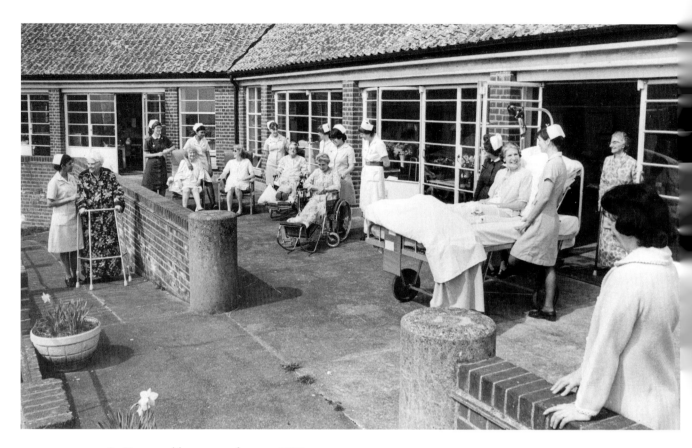

Sr Simes and her team of nurses, 1980s.

The key players in this energetic event were Staff Nurse Sharon Cooper, Sister Jenny Yexley, David Woodward, the hospital driver, with Roger Corti on backroom preparations.

There were many great supporters of St Vincent's and in each element of the hospital there are stories to be told. Within the administrative area the marketing team Jim Trigwell and Sandra Whitehead made an impression on the work attracted to St Vincent's in the latter 1990s.

St Vincent's over the years had many characters staying at the hospital and one such was Cyril Davenport, who retired as a long-time medical librarian at the Royal National Orthopaedic Hospital Stanmore. He was a well-respected man and after a brief period following surgery and rehabilitation decided that he wanted to stay at St Vincent's. He then became a long-standing 'resident' on one of the wards in a single room and was very happy.

Ron Teather as Hospital Secretary was key to ensuring goals were met to support the general manager, Alan Edmondson, to respond to the challenging demands of the NHS, desiring to maintain the high standards of care and value for money. Eddie Nolan held the accounts with Colin Furness, who went on to become the company secretary in St Vincent's Nursing Home.

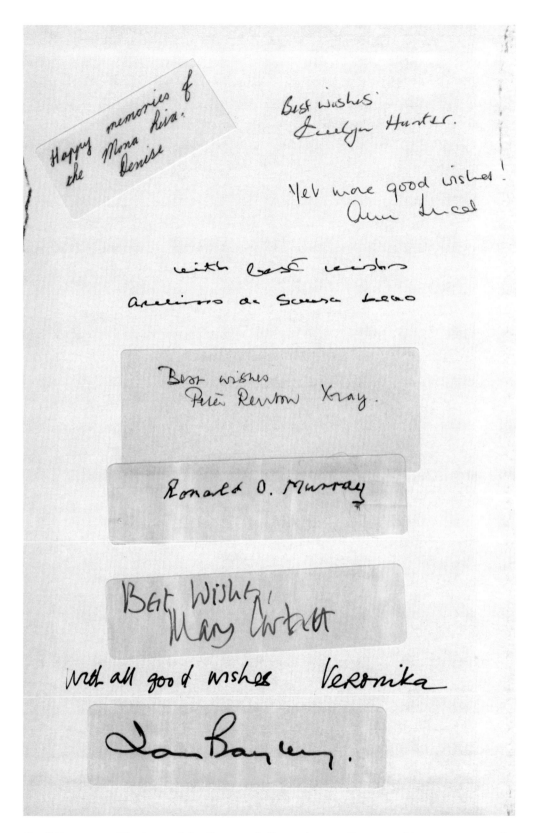

Cyril Davenport. The inset of the fly cover indicates how well respected he was amongst the orthopaedic greats. The names include some significant orthopaedic surgeons: Ronald Murray, Ian Bayley FRCS, Ginger Wilson FRCS and Dennis Stoker.

Within the clinical areas there are so many significant people; the surgeons and the support staff; nurses, notably Night Sisters Petal Connell and Rose Barr, and Maureen Eaton, Violetta Laraya, senior nurse Sr Christine Wholley DC OPD, Irene Heywood Jones tutor and OPD, Sr Mary Jo Powell DC, radiography, Catherine Gardner, Anne Griffin, occupational health, Jenny Usher (Yexley), recovery, and Sheila Swain, private block. Gail Baldwin was the physiotherapy superintendent for many years and Daphne Hiles her deputy.

Occupational therapists were Sr Nolan Umbretta DC for three years; Jean Hall who retired in 1994 and assistant Juliette Hurran. Not to be forgotten is the sterling contribution by ancillary staff, catering and housekeeping teams. Audrey Hogben was the telephonist for 16 years, followed by Barbara Rogers and Moira Newman.

Above left:: Anne Griffin, occupational health nurse, and Sr Carmel Cussen.

Above right: Receptionist Moira Newman.

Below: Catering team, including Craig de Venney.

Matrons Sr Angela Murray DC, Sr Carmel Cussen DC and Jacquie Scott.

Maddalena Noviello was also a notable character and retired after 28 years as a member of the housekeeping team in 1998.

Sr Angela Murray celebrated her golden anniversary as a Daughter of Charity in 1993, having started her Community life at St Vincent's in the 1940s. She had been a Ward Sister, Tutor, and Matron, and returned to the Sisters' House in retirement in 1993, after a rich and fulfilling life sharing her talents and skills with all those with whom she worked.

Sr Carmel was the Matron when Sr Angela returned to St Vincent's and when Sr Carmel retired Jacquie Scott took over as the first lay person to be Matron and then Chief Executive.

1994 – WATERSHED MOMENT

During 1994 the Hillingdon Local Authority Planning Committee granted St Vincent's outline planning permission for houses and flats to be built on the Wiltshire Lane site, allowing the hospital to realise funds to develop the orthopaedic surgical vision to secure its future.

Despite so much going on, the hospital continued its daily routine and mission to serve the local population and minister to the sick.

Veronica Makins, a member of the Grail Community in Pinner, came to convalesce after surgery. During this convalescence she recalled her first visit to St Vincent's some 60 years previously, when St Teresa Fraser, the first Matron, had been in charge.

Veronica spent a couple of weeks as a volunteer in 1927 and recalls meeting Sr Teresa. She had heard that Sr Teresa had been involved in orthopaedic nursing before she had become a Daughter of Charity and so had significant experience of looking after children with TB and other orthopaedic diseases.

Sr Teresa received Veronica and five other volunteers in the dining room at St Vincent's on a dark, cold December night. Sr Teresa handed out their rations: a jar of jam, a jar of marmalade, a pot of sugar and some butter. 'This must last a week.' Then she spelled out the order of the day. Rise at 7am, go to Mass, eat breakfast and be on the wards by 9am. After 4.15pm they were free.

Veronica really only had time to focus on the areas she was assigned to; her own room, the Chapel, St Joseph's Ward and the dining room.

The dining room served many purposes; it was a place to eat, a discussion centre, a community room, a reception room and immediately in front of the dining room was the conservatory, in which some of the nurses used to roller skate in the evenings.

As a volunteer she wore a white coat to assist the lay nurse and two Daughters of Charity. The Sisters wore white overalls as well as their blue habits and their flyaway head gear.

St Joseph's Ward for boys aged 6–12 was not how she had imagined a ward would be. The walls were all made of wood and the fourth wall was completely open to the winter's cold, considered necessary for TB cases in those days.

On the first morning, it was snowing hard so my first job was to brush the snow off the bed covers. We remade the beds, which often led to surprising finds, like a piece of bread and jam under a pillow, or an egg halfway down the bed, then we pushed all the beds into a semi-circle and changed the ward into a classroom. At 10.30am lessons began, the snow still falling and the teachers sitting in their winter coats. There was, of course, no radio, let alone TV, within the hospital or on the wards.

Our work as volunteers was naturally unskilled. It involved every sort of odd job, washing dirty sheets in a bath and wringing them out by hand, scrubbing floors, tidying cupboards, rolling bandages, talking to patients – whatever the nurse in charge thought necessary.

By then we were certainly ready for lunch in our multi-purpose dining room and fortunately we got on well with the nurses. Some volunteers used to rush up to London once 4.15pm arrived. I never did, I found it exhausting enough without that too!

Destruction of the splint room with Tom Baldwin and Stephen Lovell.

> One morning going to Chapel for Mass when it was snowing heavily, I heard a voice saying, 'Miss! Miss!' I looked down to find a small boy lying in the snow, unable to rise because his legs were enclosed in heavy iron splints. I had to lift him up and carry him into the Chapel.

Veronica was glad of the opportunity for the short experience at St Vincent's and says she learned a lot from the courage and cheerfulness of the small patients, who seldom complained and seemed able to see the funny side of life despite lying in bed in uncomfortable frames and splints.

Changes within the wider world, spiralling costs and the need to ensure value for money, together with the impending general election were to have a significant impact on the future of St Vincent's.

The year 1998 included the first experience of arson with, the splint room being set alight. Fortunately no one was hurt. However, patients were evacuated from St Mary's Ward as a precaution. The destruction of all the shoe lasts was hard to bear.

The Garden Fete for 1998 was to be the last, although at the time we did not realise this. We had a wonderful day and the public response and support from all the staff was in keeping with tradition.

Sr Carmel Cussen DC after many years as Matron was to take early retirement in 1998. She had been a great advocate for the patients and supporting high-quality care, expecting only the best, following in the footsteps of her Daughters of Charity predecessors.

Sr Carmel recalls her life at St Vincent's:

I arrived at St Vincent's from Liverpool where I had been nursing surgical patients and expected a similar situation. What I found could not have been more different. It was a beautiful summer's day.

The gardens were at their best and everyone I met was so friendly, I had never seen a place like it before! Sr Angela was the Matron. Firstly she asked, 'Have you got your orthopaedic certificate?' I said no. Her answer was, 'Well, you had better get it.' That meant more study, which I was not very thrilled about. During general training we always kept as far away as possible from the orthopaedic patients. All the traction and plasters looked very complicated so I certainly left that to people who were better able than I. My first workplace was the private block and recovery unit with Sr Catherine who was a wonderful Ward Sister and teacher.

I remember the beautiful summer evenings and the large glass patio doors of the wards open to spectacular views over to Harrow. Without houses at the bottom of the hill there was nothing to obstruct the view. No doors were locked as there was no fear of intruders but it was a very different situation when I retired as Matron in 1997.

I was Ward Sister on St Michael's Ward for older boys and worked closely with Miss Kenna in charge of St Paul's for the younger boys.

I completed a diploma in ward management and teaching at the Royal College of Nursing and enjoyed the course and met some wonderful people, many of whom stayed in touch and were very helpful and supportive to the work of St Vincent's.

After that it was back to the private block and recovery wards with Jean Ferguson as the senior Ward Sister. The next few years were very happy with good teamwork and we enjoyed helping the orthopaedic students that Sr Clare allocated to us.

Sr Angela was an examiner for the Joint Examination Board, the body responsible for awarding the Orthopaedic Nursing Certificate and Diploma. It was her great desire that Sr Clare and I should join her in this work. Through this we learned about the wider orthopaedic world and in the course of our duties as examiners we visited most of the other orthopaedic hospitals which at that time were flourishing.

We examined at the Robert Jones and Agnes Hunt Hospital in Oswestry, Lord Mayor Treloar in Alton Hampshire, Princess Elizabeth Hospital, Exeter,

WINDSOR CASTLE

From:

HER MAJESTY THE QUEEN

Acknowledgement to be sent to
PRIVY-PURSE OFFICE,
BUCKINGHAM PALACE S.W.1.

Above left: Gift card from the Privy Purse.

Left: Easter celebration daffodils.

and of course the Royal National Orthopaedic Hospital in Stanmore which continues to do wonderful work in orthopaedics.

Life went on at St Vincent's through many changes and several health service reorganisations. All of this affected St Vincent's but change was necessary. I was asked to take on the role of deputy matron. By that time Colin Carne was the hospital secretary and Sr Elizabeth Armstrong was the Matron. Mr Carne was a very competent person who always had the best interests of St Vincent's at heart. He always gave his full support to the Daughters of Charity and in particular to the Matron.

Peter Rodgers had been working at the Regional Health Authority and was involved with St Vincent's. He later joined the Board as a Trustee and gave many years of devoted service until his retirement in 1998.

Dr Catherine Hollman and David Blythe were loyal friends, as was David Purser. David Purser was welcomed to the AGM at the Nursing Home when we celebrated Alan Edmondson's 30-year association with St Vincent's.

The next 20 years were very busy and I was appointed Matron in 1978. Our inspection team kept us on a safe path and they came from the Health Authority and were a great support to us and included Paul Taylor, administrator, Dr Eddie Jones, environmental health officer, and Betty Froud, area nurse.

Her Majesty the Queen presented St Vincent's with an annual gift – and each spring 50 bunches of daffodils arrive. They are always treasured and admired by the residents and staff and have long been a tradition and there is great anticipation of their arrival each year. They light up the Chapel and the home and mark the great Easter celebration.

FR WILLIAM BROWN

Fr Brown was a very popular Chaplain and visited all the patients in every ward and department every day despite the weather. He always had a good word and a little story and was a prolific writer. Many patients of St Vincent's would have one of his booklets on faith and prayer.

There were many wonderful stories over the years, far too many to mention. However one patient while recovering from surgery found the energy and professional hierarchies within a hospital environment was too good a plot to miss. She observed everything that was going on in the ward and then wrote a play called 'Bonaventure', a murder mystery and the characters and plot were developed around the staff in the wards and departments at the time.

One of our most important projects was to use the former babies' ward to provide 12 beds for children with special needs, six for long-term care and six for respite. With the passing of the years the needs of the families changed and social services made other provisions, increasingly moving away from institutional care.

Later the building was once more upgraded and converted into a unit for care of elderly people, called Fraser House in memory of Sr Teresa Fraser, the first Matron of the hospital. The years were very busy and passed quickly. Brigid Haig was the final Ward Sister prior to its closure. Sr Carmel Cussen DC Matron for many years said that she had the most wonderful staff and colleagues who worked tirelessly and without whom St Vincent's would never have managed to achieve all that was accomplished.

Fr William Brown, Chaplain.

Sr Carmel goes on to say that it is very encouraging to see that the ethos of St Vincent's and all that we tried to achieve through good relationships and support for each other over the many years has continued now in to a new St Vincent's in the nursing home.

JACQUIE SCOTT

Following in these footsteps was not going to be easy. In the same year, 1998, Jacquie Scott, a Catholic and an orthopaedic nurse with significant clinical and management experience, joined the Board of St Vincent's and became the final Matron and CEO/Director of Nursing.

The hospital continued to provide orthopaedic care to the community by maintaining contracts from different Health Authorities. However, the political scene was changing, for in 1997 the new Labour government had made altera-tions to healthcare provision that would impact enormously on St Vincent's.

St Vincent's carried on and tried many approaches in what was to become the final year. Fraser House was closed due to reduction in funding from the Health Authority and this displaced many elderly folk.

Staff were dispersed across the hospital in other clinical roles while the Ward Sister was supported to facilitate a smooth transition for the residents. Orthopaedic surgery finally ceased in 1999, primarily due to financial constraints and a change of political direction.

The Board of Management continued to maintain the services of the hospital and for a further 12 months were able to maximise the NHS 'winter pressure' resource, St Vincent's providing clinical support as a step-down service for Northwick Park and the Hillingdon Hospital orthopaedic service. Patients under-

FRASER HOUSE

ST. VINCENT'S ORTHOPAEDIC HOSPITAL

PINNER, MIDDLESEX

Fraser House is a newly refurbished unit for the care of the elderly, situated within the grounds of St. Vincent's Orthopaedic Hospital.

Fraser House marketing booklet.

Putting St Vincent's 'back on the map'

● WORK FOR COMMUNITY: *New nursing director, Jacquie Scott.*   98/70

A DIRECTOR of nursing at St Vincent's Hospital is looking forward to helping to introduce a community care programme to help the disabled.

Jacquie Scott hopes the service, aimed at Hillingdon people with chronic disabilities, will strengthen St Vincent's role as a community hospital.

Miss Scott, who started work at the hospital in Wiltshire Lane, Eastcote, this month (January), said: "We have been putting a plan together this month.

"This will be a community facility for people under 65, people who need long-term rehabilitation and who need more help with activities.

"It is aimed at people who have had strokes or car accidents, who need support.

"It will be getting St Vincent's back on the map."

She hopes the programme will include physiotherapy, occupational therapy and speech therapy.

The hospital wants to work with Hillingdon Hospital to put the plan into action.

New Head of Hospital, Director of Nursing and Chief Executive.

took their planned surgery at the acute hospital and transferred to St Vincent's for specialist rehabilitation with qualified orthopaedic nurses, physiotherapy and occupational therapists. Marilyn Bates managed to keep the X-ray department functioning until the end of 1999, thus ending a remarkable era of radiographic service to the locality since 1912.

Despite concerns, St Vincent's carried on doing the business of the day.

Sustaining the staff and running costs was extremely challenging and a massive financial risk. However, it was felt by the staff and general public that St Vincent's should not be allowed to close and it was hoped that the local health economy would reconsider the position it played in the clinical orthopaedic world. It was

Left: Marilyn Bates, senior radiographer.

Below: Official reopening of the hospital shop, 1998. Left to right: Margaret Bayliss; Joyce White; Gail Baldwin, physiotherapy superintendent; Sr Christine Wholley; Sr Mary Jo; Anne Griffin, occupational health nurse; Sr Jenny Yexley and Catherine Gardiner.

Below left: Diane Holmes, Matron's personal assistant.

Below right: Left to right: Sr Mary Jo DC, Jean Dixon and Margaret Bayliss.

Right: Left to right: Fr Brown, Sr Joseph and Sr Jane Doran DC, Sister servant.

apparent this was not sustainable for the future and that the running costs were far outweighing the revenue required to continue.

The hospital had also to consider the future of other services that had been a significant part of St Vincent's, the Templeton Unit which was a unique and special service which was a day centre and refuge for carers of those who had been affected by early onset Alzheimer's. The unit was very popular and a very successful service and made a significant contribution to the community. However, the Health Authority did not consider it enough to sustain the whole site and of course the small income that it made was not within the St Vincent's accounts.

Within the site, too, was a successful, privately owned children's nursery which had been a part of St Vincent's for many years and was a favourite amongst the locals for offering excellent childcare – this eventually was re-sited in the school down the hill – but this along with the Hillingdon Autism Centre was destined to be moved by the Health Authority and council to other locations within the borough. If St Vincent's had any hope of a future the small businesses had to vacate the premises. The site remained derelict for five years.

The Chief Executives of Hillingdon Health Authority and the Community Healthcare Trust, along with the Nursing Home Registration Inspectorate, worked with the Board to propose a suitable outcome.

The Board was desperately trying to ensure it could keep the hospital going but the financial burden had become critical and all the staff were very loyal but, despite many petitions, a prime-time slot on BBC South-East News and an adjournment debate in the House of Commons supported by our local Member of Parliament John Wilkinson, it was rapidly looking bleak. It was doubtful that staff salaries would be paid – income was limited – and with no apparent hope of new income, the Board, after numerous meetings with the CEOs of Hillingdon, Harrow and Hillingdon Healthcare Trust and the Local Authority, decided with great heartache that St Vincent's would be forced to close.

Calculations were made regarding the costs of redundancy and we knew if we carried on we would not be able to meet these obligations – the news statement was published and the staff informed of the decision. This weighed heavily on the Board and, as the CEO and Matron, Jacquie found it heartbreaking to see the extent of devastation this news had on staff, many of whom had been serving St Vincent's for a lifetime.

The management team maintained its focus and, with support from the local health economy, in particular the Healthcare Community Trust, we were able to TUPE (Transfer of Undertakings Protection of Employment) across a number of staff to NHS posts and those remaining were made redundant.

The hospital closed with a phased timetable. St Vincent's managed to provide the 'post-operative' management of patients from the local hospitals following orthopaedic surgery because of the acute bed crisis and was kept going for a short while with NHS 'winter pressure' work, but once this ceased in November 1999 we had no choice but to start winding down.

The physiotherapy 'outpatient' service maintained activity and it was hoped we might be able to continue this service as it was a major provider in the locality. Gail Baldwin maintained the morale of the therapy team and supported the services even after the main wards closed to surgery and inpatient rehabilitation.

However, the Primary Care Groups (PCGs) which were led by local general practitioners were not prepared to support this service with any service-level agreements, so it was the end of March 2000 when the doors finally closed.

As there was so much support for the hospital, many local people reacted angrily to the decision made by the Board and a number of people made their feelings known. It was a difficult time in the history of St Vincent's. Jacquie Scott led the 'front-facing' redundancy and the final running-down of services, ensuring people were cared for and helped to make decisions about their own futures, but felt the brunt of the anger.

The Board at the time made a vow that it would ensure that, despite the closure and what would be seen as a period of sadness, St Vincent's would start up again and make certain that the name and good works would continue. There were many sceptics who felt we were incompetent handling the hospital, resulting in

Gail Baldwin, superintendent physiotherapist.

the devastating outcome. However, with no funds left, but a fierce determination, we were able to do just as we had declared and a new life was put back into the spirit of St Vincent's.

The Daughters of Charity continued living in the Sisters' House and maintained their presence to assure the staff and local people that they believed St Vincent's could carry on. The general practitioner Anthony O'Connor and his wife Elizabeth were great friends for many years and it was a sad time for all.

However, once the site completely closed it was becoming derelict and it was not a safe place. It was decided that the Sisters would need to move back to Provincial House in Mill Hill and support us from there whilst the redevelopment plans took shape.

Jacquie moved in to the Sister's House to provide some security and oversee the on-site activity.

Fr Tom Harrington was the last Chaplain in St Vincent's Hospital before its final closure. He used to say the gates were being locked when he arrived! However, he made an excellent contribution to pastoral ministry at St Vincent's and kept in contact with local parishes. He is a very special person who still maintains an interest in St Vincent's in its new life as a nursing home. Fr Harrington retired to Ireland.

Colin Furness, the accounts officer, became one of a small team that facilitated the drive to ensure St Vincent's was able to remain on the existing site whilst still maintaining its 'charitable objects':

My first recollection of St Vincent's dates back to about 1964. My cousin had been admitted because one of his legs was shorter than the other; or was it because one was longer than the other – but then again would anyone know whether he was destined to be 4ft 6in or 7ft 9in?

However, they were able to put things right and I was taken by my mum to visit him (he actually ended up 5ft 8in, by the way). My overriding memory of my visit was the nuns with their huge white hats which scared the living daylights out of me, and I swear they gave me nightmares for weeks after.

Anyway, I can say that my cousin seemed much better after his stay at the hospital, so they must have done something right, and little did I know at the time that some many years later St Vincent's would become a major part of my world.

Having spent the first 23 years of my working life in the printing industry I was devastated when the recession of the early 1990s ended my career. I was redundant at the age of 40. After just a year in the motor industry I was about to cross paths with St Vincent's once again.

I remember well the day I was called for interview, eventually finding the place at the top of the hill and seeing the mixture of buildings that formed the hospital site. Every building was different; in style, in shape, colour and differing building material, it was just as if the brief for every new building that had sprung up was to make it unique and at variance with those already on the site!

I was offered the job and my career at St Vincent's began in May 1995. My enduring early memory was how friendly the people were, which was not always so in my previous working life; also, how much St Vincent's was loved by its patients past and present. I think the quality of the staff employed at the hospital could really be summed up by the maintenance team, who were a real 'motley crew' but could have probably rebuilt the *Titanic* from scrap material, given the task they had keeping all the old plant and machinery going at St Vincent's.

It was a sad part of St Vincent's history when the hospital had to close in March 2000 and at that time it was impossible to imagine what would rise from the ashes. I stayed on part-time, tasked with helping in the process of building something on the plot of the old hospital.

I remember many a cold and sad visit, coming to the site not knowing how much further it had deteriorated, whether there had been another break-in with another mess to clear up. However, the loyal team charged with the task of creating the new nursing home kept going, sometimes seeming against overwhelming odds, but eventually the goal of the new nursing home was achieved and thus began the new chapter in the life of St Vincent's.

I began full-time at St Vincent's again as Company Secretary/Accountant in April 2000 and it has been heartening to see another great team of staff that will keep the St Vincent's story going strong for the next 100 years and more.

THE FOURTH GENERATION:
2005—2012

— RISING FROM THE ASHES – LITERALLY —

As there were many comings and goings on the site and a number of unwelcome visitors, Jacquie recalls that she had developed a welcome relationship with the local Metropolitan Police, who were very supportive and visited the site on a number of occasions following unruly local children breaking windows and generally making a nuisance of themselves.

There was also someone using the facilities in one of the empty wards; I knew there was someone about on site but could never catch them out. Then, one Sunday afternoon, whilst walking around the site, I found the uninvited visitor, or at least evidence of someone.

I noticed a green garden hose connected to an outside tap and followed this into a door which had been previously padlocked. Once inside the building it became apparent that someone had been doing their washing, with clothes carefully hung on all the open cupboard doors in the kitchen area.

Despite having turned off all the services from the main service point, the gas and water had been reconnected and a metal bin was sitting on the stove with washing boiling away inside. As I progressed further down the corridor, following the green hose, it ended in what used to be a bathroom. Underneath the bath with the side panel removed, was a three-bar heater lying sideways and a bath full of steaming water – clearly someone was about to complete their Sunday ablutions!

I did not see anyone but called the police. However, I am almost certain I was being watched and of course they – and all the washing too – left the site!

Over the years while we worked with the Hillingdon planning office and a continual change of planning officers – some 14 over the six-year period – there were many stories of night-time shenanigans, and some evenings when coming home from a night out I would be conscious of being watched. I once saw the red-orange glow of a cigarette in the distance where someone was standing in the shadows as I hurried into the Sisters' House. After that particular evening an alarm was fitted.

When in 2000 it was clear that government policy was forcing St Vincent's (and undoubtedly other bodies/institutions) to close, the Board of Trustees/ Directors declared that they would do everything in their power to ensure the tradition of St Vincent's continued on the same site. It was agreed that a nursing home would be built and that the reputation of St Vincent's would be continued for a further 100 years.

Following the closure no money was left, almost £1.1 million having been spent on redundancy costs and ensuring all outstanding debts were cleared. It was undoubtedly a difficult period. The small team spent time ensuring that the equipment that was left was either sold on to other organisations or donated to good causes so that very little was wasted or destroyed.

The time for a significant change was then seen as inevitable.

The Board of Trustees included John Davern, Chairman, who had been actively involved on the Board at St Vincent's for 34 years, and Alan Edmondson, Trustee, involved for 33 years, along with Trustees Jacquie Scott and Bernard Luckhurst, the Company Secretary/Accountant, Colin Furness, Ray Plummer and Susan Taylor. It took six eventful years working as a team with the intention of ensuring that the development would succeed.

Above left: Extraordinary measures for Sunday ablutions.

Above right: Ray Plummer, external adviser to the management team, previously estates manager.

Left: Signing the contract to begin the build: Peter Williams, surveyor, and John Davern, Chairman.

Susan Taylor reflects on her experience and time at the hospital:

> I have very fond memories of my time at St Vincent's, first of all working part-time as a medical secretary for some of the consultant surgeons and latterly as secretary to the main Board. Having lived in Pinner all my life the history of St Vincent's has always been of interest to me and it was a valuable experience working as part of a team to witness its survival and ultimate transition to that of a nursing home.

By selling some of its own land the charity funded the building of the 60-bed nursing home, which opened in July 2006.

The period during the building phase was not without its challenges not least of all the planning issues, vandalism and a major fire at the outset of the new development. The fire in July 2004 set the project timetable back considerably. However, undeterred, the team carried on and eventually gained momentum.

Jacquie recalls one evening having returned 'home' to the Sister's House from a dinner with work colleagues that it was a balmy summer's evening:

> I found I could not settle and was quite restless. As I was sleeping in the front of the Sisters' House on the first floor near the front door I was lying in bed and noticed an orange glow outside. As I could not sleep I got up to look out the window and to my horror saw that the main building which had been surrounded by 'clapper boards' in readiness for demolition was alight with flames roaring into the night sky.
>
> The London Fire Brigade were outstanding in their prompt response and struggled to identify a water source and so had to pump water up Fore Street in order to have enough water pressure to dowse the flames. In all it took three days to extinguish the fire – and the impact was devastating.
>
> There were many fire engines and numerous firemen working for hours to contain the fire and the smoke could be seen for miles around. Thankfully no one was injured.

The following sequence of images shows the realisation of all the determination, planning and hard work coming to fruition that the first Trustees visualised as the site for the future of St Vincent's carrying on the 'Objects' and Mission of the Charity.

As the project manager, Jacquie was very keen to be involved in all aspects and took the responsibility seriously. 'I learned many new skills, including brick-laying, interior design, plastering and the rudiments of procurement and I also assisted with digging the foundations.'

Left: A fire engulfs St Vincent's.

Below: Hands-on action for Jacquie Scott, Trustee and project manager for site development: digging the foundations.

Bottom: St Vincent's is beginning to re-emerge, 2005.

The project team, including Richard Heath, architect, Peter Williams, surveyor, and the site foreman Neil Woodhouse, were committed to ensuring St Vincent's was perfect and fit for purpose.

The only vestige left, a great bell, was kept, and today you find it on a pedestal by the cemetery, making it the great symbol of the tenacity of St Vincent's.

Above: St Vincent's front entrance, 2005.

Left: First blessing of the bell.

Above: St Vincent's bell being re-sited back on St Vincent's soil.

Below: St Vincent's, summer 2006.

Wintertime.

MARCH 2006, STAFF RECRUITMENT FROM THE LOCALITY COMMENCED

St Vincent's is now a beautiful purpose-built nursing home with en-suite facilities, separate dining rooms and lounges, an activities programme, wonderful landscaped gardens and an 80-seat Chapel and a rekindled spirit which has been set towards a further century.

The Daughters were the first to come over the threshold in July 2006 when St Vincent's Nursing Home opened its doors and Sr Gladys Monk DC was the first Daughter officially over the threshold and so the first resident.

Cardinal Cormac Murphy O'Connor opened and blessed the new Catholic home for retired elderly laity and religious in Eastcote on Tuesday 19 September 2006. Holy Mass was celebrated by Fr Michael Connor, parish priest of St Thomas More Church, Eastcote, with six concelebrants from the local parishes.

Chairman John Davern and other Members of the Board and management team, led by Matron Shiria Halsey, greeted His Eminence and took great pleasure in showing him around the home. The Cardinal said that 'he would like to book his place for the future', saying further 'how wonderful the home was'.

Above: Sr Gladys Monk DC, the first resident to walk over the threshold, with Sr Sarah King Turner DC on her left and Sr Carmel Cussen DC on her right.

Left: Rev. Michael Connor, parish priest of St Thomas More, Eastcote.

Below: The blessing of St Vincent's Nursing Home, 2006.

ST VINCENT'S NURSING HOME

THE CHAIRMAN AND BOARD OF DIRECTORS
REQUEST THE PLEASURE OF THE COMPANY OF

AT THE
BLESSING AND OFFICIAL OPENING
OF
ST VINCENT'S NURSING HOME
BY HIS EMINENCE
CARDINAL CORMACK MURPHY-O'CONNOR PH.L,STL
TUESDAY 19 SEPTEMBER 2006

Holy Sacrifice of the Mass   10.00am
Blessing of the Home   11.15am

RSVP
Jacquie Scott
St Vincent's Nursing Home
Wiltshire Lane, Eastcote Pinner
HA5 2EP

Above: Celebrating Holy Mass.

Below: John Davern, Chairman, receiving the Pro Eclesia Medal from Archbishop Cormac Murphy O'Connor, 2006.

During the celebration the Cardinal presented the Chairman with an award from the Catholic Church for his hard work and determination in ensuring that St Vincent's continued for a further century. John Davern received the Pro Eclesia et Pontifice Medal which was conferred by his Holiness Pope Benedict XVI.

Above: Administrative staff at St Vincent's Nursing Home. Left to right: Annie, Linda and Susan.

Below: Sr Catherine Pitt OFM and Sr Mary Jo Powell DC.

Above: Sisters enjoying afternoon tea: Sr Gladys Monk DC is second on the left.

Below: Llewellyn Heywood Jones and Cathy O'Sullivan, activities co-ordinator.

Christmas Fayre helpers Mrs Claudette Keane, Sr Aine McGuinness DC and Cathy O'Sullivan.

Left: Sr Josephine O'Mahoney at the Christmas Fayre.

Below: Face-painting.

Above: Deputy Matron Valerie Campbell.

Left: Sr Joseph DC at Christmas.

Margaret and Alan Edmondson with Paul Castle, Barclays Bank manager.

Above: Residents enjoying the children dancing.

Below: Irish dancers entertaining the residents, with Ava Mahoney.

Nursing home celebrates in true Irish style

THERE were reels and jigs aplenty at a nursing home where dancers performed to help celebrate St Patrick's Day.

St Vincent's Nursing Home, Wiltshire Lane, Eastcote, enjoyed a day's events of Irish dancing from Barrett Semple-Morris School of Irish Dancing.

Social activities worker, Cathy O'Sullivan, organises these type of days once a month to entertain the residents.

She said: "It was a fantastic day and all of the residents and their guests enjoyed it. "

The day on Friday, began with four-six-year-olds dancing first to warm up the crowd, then six-10 year olds, followed lastly by 10 year olds and up.

Past event days include an Italian day, and an English day all in celebration of St Vincent's diverse and multicultural atomosphere.

Ava Mahoney, seven, jigs at St Vincent's Nursing Home, Eastcote.
The young dancers were invited down from the Barrett Semple-Morris School of Irish Dancing as part of the St Patrick's Day celebrations.
Picture by Toby Vandevelde D14667-3.

– LIFE AT ST VINCENT'S IN THE 21ST CENTURY –

St Vincent's Nursing Home now offers residential and nursing care for people over 60 years of age who require support in a homely environment. It also offers a home with a Catholic ethos and daily Mass which welcomes retired religious and clergy as well as the local laity. The home has an excellent primary care service which is provided by Dr Geraldine Golden MB BCH BAO LRCPS DCH MRCGP and Dr Michael Abu MD FRCOG and their practice nurses Elaine and Mary.

Above: Visiting relatives Lucy, Jim, Rene and Ben.

Below: Piper and Scottish dancing.

Musicians at the annual 'birthday' party.

Opposite above: Centenary year – re-enacting the journey to Pinner.

Opposite below: Variety club.

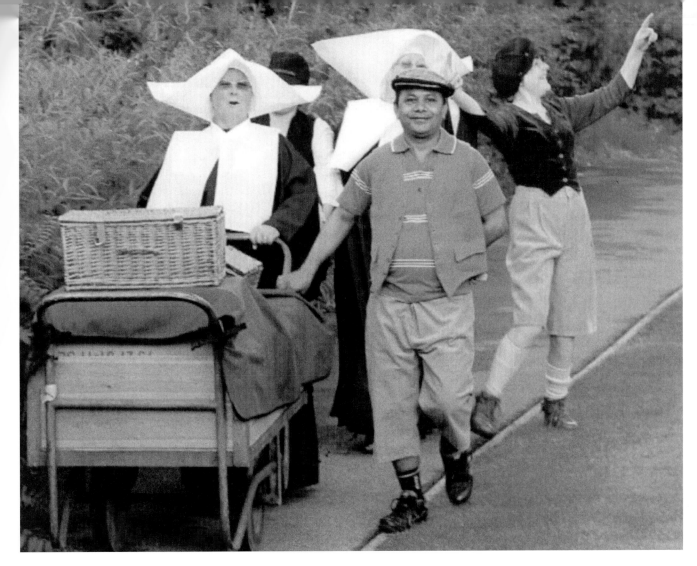

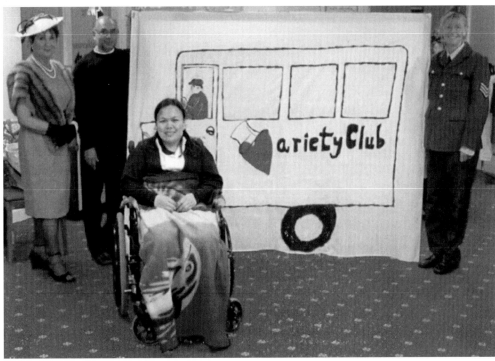

Matrons Jacquie Scott, Sr Carmel Cussen DC and Shiria Halsey.

OUR MISSION

Our mission is to promote the home as a centre of excellence, where our residents receive high-quality care and are the focus of everything we do. This is achieved through meeting our residents' needs, as they perceive them, and striving to improve our services and environment.

OUR VALUES

Each resident is considered as an individual with their own special needs and wishes.

It is our philosophy to ensure that everyone is treated with respect and dignity and that they will be cared for until natural death.

All staff shall use and develop their knowledge and skills to improve our residents' well-being and to provide professional support to everyone.

St Vincent's prides itself on ensuring that the whole person is cared for, including their emotional, social and spiritual needs.

The Grace of St Vincent and a little help from a few amazing people along the way has kept the 'light' of St Vincent's in Pinner going and long may it last.

Sisters standing outside the front entrance to the hospital.

Left: Centenary Ball, 2012: Chairman Jacquie Scott, Cardinal Cormack Murphy O'Connor and Matron Shiria Halsey.

Below: 2012 Centenary Ball invitation.

St Vincent's Centenary Summer Ball
12th May 2012

*In the presence of His Eminence
Cardinal Cormack Murphy O'Connor
at
Moor Park Mansion
Northwood, WD3 1QN*

*Reception at 6:30pm
Dinner at 7:30pm*

*Music : Berkeley Square Society Band
Dress Code: Black Tie*

Carriages : 12:30 midnight

SIGNIFICANT PEOPLE

MATRONS OF ST VINCENT'S

1936–1942	Sr Teresa Fraser DC
1942–1949	Sr Mary Neville DC
1949–1950	Sr Vincent Neilan DC
1950–1966	Sr Angela Murray DC
1967–1972	Sr Vincent Neilan DC
1972–1974	Sr Genevieve Bergin DC
1974–1977	Sr Elizabeth Armstrong DC
1978–1997	Sr Carmel Cussen DC
1997–2000	Jacqueline Scott
2006–present	Shiria Halsey

BOARD CHAIRMEN OF ST VINCENT'S

1909–1942	Sir Cecil Pereira
1912–1930	Bishop Bidwell
1931–1948	Sir James Calder CBE
1948–1957	Richard Stokes
1958–1969	Captain F.H. Formby
1969–1980	Anthony L. Janssens
1981–1987	Ben Turner
1987–1990	Alan Edmondson
1991–1998	Jim Brown
1998–1999	Professor Malone Lee
1999–2011	John B. Davern
2011–present	Jacqueline A. Scott

CHAPLAINS OF ST VINCENT'S

1912–1922	Fr Hurley
1923–1935	Fr J. Heditch
1936–1939	Fr Harrington
1940–1942	Fr A. Stewart
1942–1945	Fr C. Boddy
1945–1957	Fr Patrick O'Daly
1958–1960	Fr John Galvin

1960–1964	Fr John Bebb
1966–1976	Canon Hathaway
1977–1979	Canon D.M.J. Crowley
1980–1980	Fr Collingwood
1981–1998	Fr William Brown
1998–1999	Fr Tom Harrington
2006–2008	Fr Ray Armstrong
2010–present	Fr Ted Wildsmith

Principal Trustees of St Vincent's, 1907–2000

Sir Cecil Pereira
Arthur Coppinger
Mrs Howden
Mr Potter
Mr Trapp
Miss Margaret Fraser
Sir James Calder
Mrs Henry Hope
His Eminence Auxiliary Bishop Bidwell
Canon Fellowes
Bishop then Cardinal Bourne, Archbishop of Westminster
His Eminence Cardinal Arthur Hinsley, Archbishop of Westminster
Rev. Canon George L. Craven then Auxiliary Bishop of Westminster
His Eminence Cardinal Bernard Griffin, Archbishop of Westminster
His Eminence Cardinal George Basil Hume, Archbishop of Westminster
Richard Stokes
Fr John Formby
Anthony Janssens
John Scanlon
Ben C.A. Turner
Peter Rodgers
Professor Malone Lee
Mgr John Coghlan
Bernard Luckhurst
Current Trustees 2012
Jacqueline Scott Chairman
Alan Edmondson
Neville Ransley
Fergal Davern
Geralyn Wynne
Neville Ransley
John Steintiz

KEY FEATURES — LANDMARKS

1907	St Vincent's Home for Crippled Boys
1909	St Vincent's Open Air – Surgical & Industrial Home
1910	Sr Teresa Fraser DC becomes Matron
1910	Surgeon Mr McCrae Aitken becomes surgeon for 36 years
1910	Mr Robert Jones becomes first honorary surgeon
1910	Ruislip Cripples' Home
1912	Fr Hurley Chaplain
1912	The Eastcote Cripples' Home – name change
1912	Charity Deeds signed
1912	Annual charge for a patient rose to 30 guineas
1913	X-ray apparatus installed
1914	Operating theatre is built
1914	Accommodation extended to include 114 boys
1914	A further 6 acres of land purchased, house became Chaplain's home
1915	Annual patient cost rose to £50
1916	X-ray put at disposal of the neighbourhood – a considerable number of wounded soldiers at the time
1918	Number of boys in the home had grown to 112
1918	Annual cost per bed increased to £60 10s
1919	Central Council for the Care of Cripples initiated
1920	St Vincent's Cripples' Home
1920	Two little Polish patients who had entered the hospital in what seemed a hopeless state of deformity are able to return to Poland with a future before them
1922	New Chapel opened, a gift from the Sisters of Charity of St Vincent's de Paul, new staff quarters built, carpenters' and fitters' shops built
1922	RNOH Stanmore country branch is opened
1923	St Matthew's Catholic Church commenced, Fr Fellowes parish priest
1923	Fr Heditch Chaplain
1924	Tailor's shop in Northwood opened, manned part-time by the older boys
1924	New name from Cripples' Home to St Vincent's Orthopaedic Hospital
1924	Ward for 20 girls opened
1924	British Orthopaedic Association (BOA) inaugurated by Mr Robert Jones FRCS and Dame Agnes Hunt

1925	Northwood, Pinner and District Hospital opened
1925	Canon Fellowes Chaplain
1927	4th Northwood Scouts and Guides started
1927	New workshops built to accommodate bootmaking, tailoring and splint-making
1928	Cost per patient increased to £90 per annum, school of massage and medical gymnastics inaugurated
1930	New girls' ward built, 24 beds at a cost of £2,500
1930	Admissions register noted 200 inpatients
1932	Nurses' Home completed
1932	Massage clinic in Ruislip opens
1933	New babies' ward built as a memorial to Bishop Bidwell, Chairman of the Hospital for 20 years
1933	Number of beds 202
1933	Average length of stay 424.5 days
1933	Nurses' salary £18 annually
1934	Jubilee Banquet – Claridges Hotel, London
1936	Fr Harrington Chaplain
1936	Original sheds begin to be replaced by brick-built wards
1937	St Paul's Ward opened
1937	St Thomas More Catholic Church Solemn Blessing and First Mass
1939	Number of beds rises to 209, including 24 men and 24 women
1939	War is declared
1939	Bed numbers rise to 219 and is designated an Emergency Medical Service
1940	Fr Stewart Chaplain
1940	Weekly inpatient rate was £2.20
1940	Rationing started and continued until 1954
1941	Chapel and sisters' refectory destroyed by crippled enemy jettisoning its load of 500lb bomb on Haste Hill, no one hurt
1942	Admissions 433
1942	Sr Neville DC is appointed Matron
1942	Rev. C. Boddy Chaplain
1943	Miss Bacon starts at the hospital
1943	New x-ray equipment installed
1944	Shortly after D-Day two casualties flown direct from France for penicillin treatment at St Vincent's
1945	Fr O'Daly Chaplain
1945	Flanagan and Allen open garden fete
1945	St Paul's Ward, used for forces casualties during the war, is returned for children
1947	School of nursing approved by General Nursing Council

1948	Fr Bebb Chaplain
1948	National Health Service began
1948	Number of beds reduced to 200
1948	Weekly patient cost increased to £4 9s 6d
1948	Mr McCrae Aitken, surgeon to the hospital for 38 years, retires
1948	Vera Lynn and Charlie Kunz open garden fete
1949	Number of beds reduced to 176
1949	Weekly cost for a patient is now £7 4s
1950	Rebuilding of St Michael's and St Margaret's Wards, outpatients waiting room
1950	Tommy Steele (musician) visits children
1952	St Michael's Ward completed
1953	St Margaret's Ward completed. Inpatient costs now £10 5s 5d
1953	Charity Ball held Tithe Farm South Harrow
1954	New operating table and light purchased
1955	Hospital now has 176 beds and admits children as babies when required
1955	Douglas Bader opens garden fete
1956	Anonymous donor pays for new road and car park construction
1959	Jimmy Edwards opens garden fete
1960	Gala Ball held
1964	Sisters' House is built
1965	Variety Club of Great Britain presents hospital with a minibus sponsored by Fred Pontin
1966	Canon Hathaway Chaplain
1967	The number of beds decreased to 141, while the weekly cost per patient increased to £30 10s 8d
1967	St Mary's Ward is opened
1970	Hospital poultry farm closes
1972	Diamond Jubilee celebrated with Mass by Cardinal Heenan
1974	The splint workshop closes
1974	Inflation pushes the weekly cost per patient up to a staggering £157.72
1976	Boot workshop contributed £12,456 to the income
1976	Ruislip Clinic closes
1977	Canon Crowley Chaplain
1977	Daily inpatient rate rises to £35
1977	Annual garden fete opened by Jessie Matthews
1977	Number of beds now 113
1980	Fr Collingwood Chaplain
1980	The number of operations performed rises to about 1,000 each year
1980	His Eminence Cardinal George Basil Hume OSB opens rehabilitation centre

1981   Fr Brown Chaplain

1990   Average length of stay five days for total hip replacement

1997   Sr Carmel Cussen DC retires

1998   Fr Tom Harrington Chaplain

1998   Jacquie Scott Matron and CEO

1998   Bob Holness opens garden fete

1999   John Davern Chairman

1999   Hospital closes

2000   Physiotherapy outpatient service closes

2006   St Vincent's Nursing Home opens

2007   Fr Ray Armstrong Chaplain, Vincentian Father

2010   Fr Ted Wildsmith Chaplain, White Father

2011   Jacquie Scott Chairman

2012   St Vincent's Centenary Ball, Moor Park Mansion

THE HOSPITAL ON THE HILL

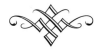

Upon the hill so proudly
This edifice once stood
For many years providing
Loving care with all that's good.
To share with those most needy
The sick and the infirm
The helpless and for those in pain
Where broken limbs are mended
And health helped to regain.
Where laughter conquered misery
Where love and kindness filled
The days where hope still lingered
For those whose fears were stilled.
With nostalgia and much sadness
We remember days gone by
But our hearts are filled with gladness
When once again we try
To emulate St Vincent
His spirit lingers still
In his our new establishment
We all aim to fulfil
Our very best to offer
Our patients one and all
May God bless our achievements,
And may we never fall.
We pray we will continue
And always will fulfil,
The hope and aspirations
of
The Hospital on the Hill.

Eileen Morton, 2013
Sr Mary Joseph Powell DC (younger Sister)